# Veritas Press

# A PHONICS MUSEUM

MARLIN & LAURIE DETWEILER
DIANE COLEMAN
NED BUSTARD
EMILY FISCHER
ERIC VANDERHOOF

ISBN 978-1-932168-62-4
Copyright ©2005 Veritas Press

Veritas Press, Lancaster, Pennsylvania
800-922-5082
www.VeritasPress.com

Third edition

# ing/ang /ong

INSTRUCTIONS:
Cut "Matisse" shapes like the ones below into potato halves. Place the potato stamps into the paint and stamp the shapes onto the paper. Blocks or strips of colored construction paper can be added to complete the effect.

SUPPLIES:
   *Paper*
   *Potatoes*
   *Tempra paint (primary colors)*

Name

## CONSONANT BLENDS

INSTRUCTIONS:
Circle the R blend at the beginning of each word.

| | | |
|---|---|---|
| frog | brick | shell |
| cat | thin | rat |
| crab | wing | ring |
| song | drum | grass |
| thing | truck | goat |

37

## CONSONANT BLENDS

Name

INSTRUCTIONS:
Copy the R blend words.

crib

frog

drum

grim

CONSONANT BLENDS

Name

INSTRUCTIONS:
Say the blend on the left with the sound on the right.

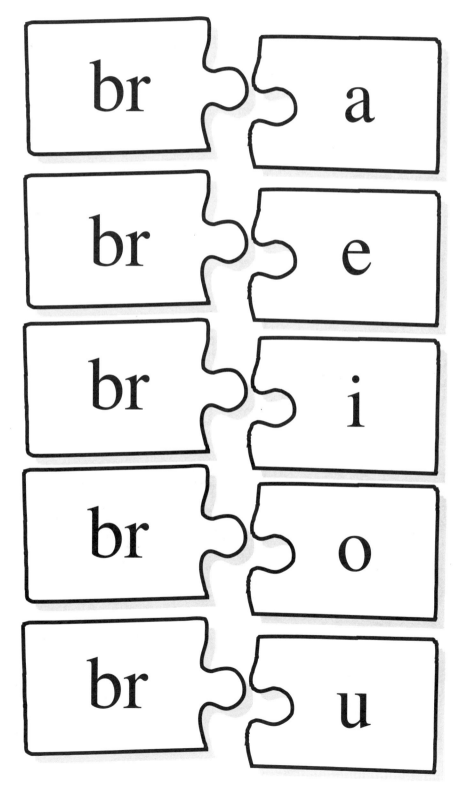

## CONSONANT BLENDS

INSTRUCTIONS:
Say the blend on the left with the sound on the right.

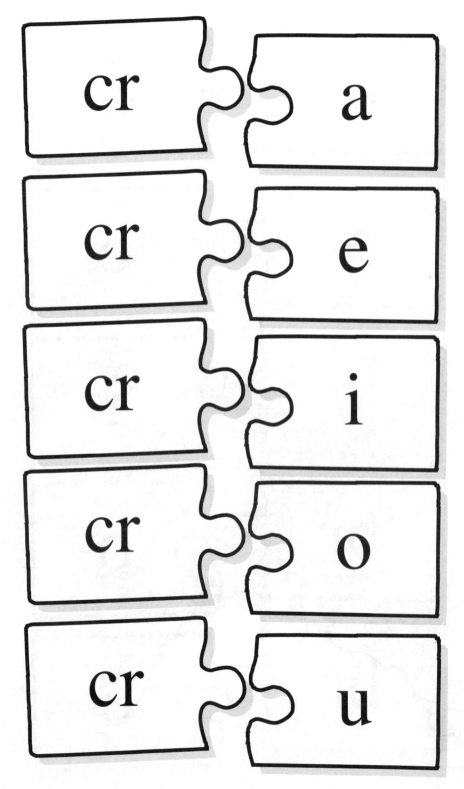

Name

## CONSONANT BLENDS

INSTRUCTIONS:
Say the blend on the left with the sound on the right.

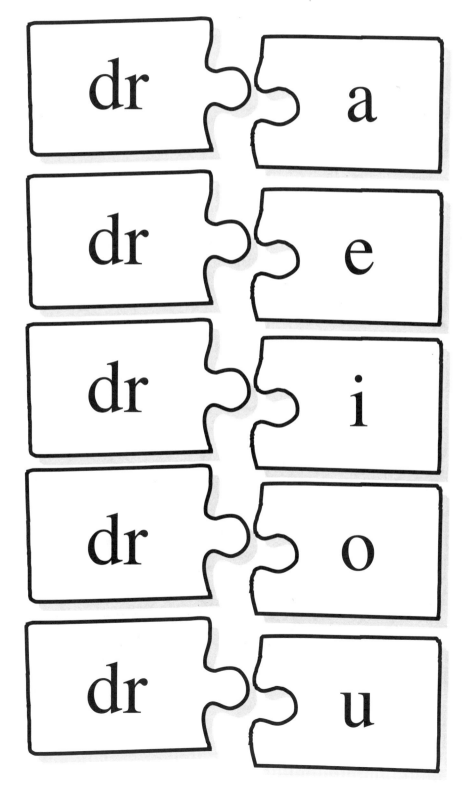

dr — a

dr — e

dr — i

dr — o

dr — u

## Consonant Blends

Name

I N S T R U C T I O N S :
Say the blend on the left with the sound on the right.

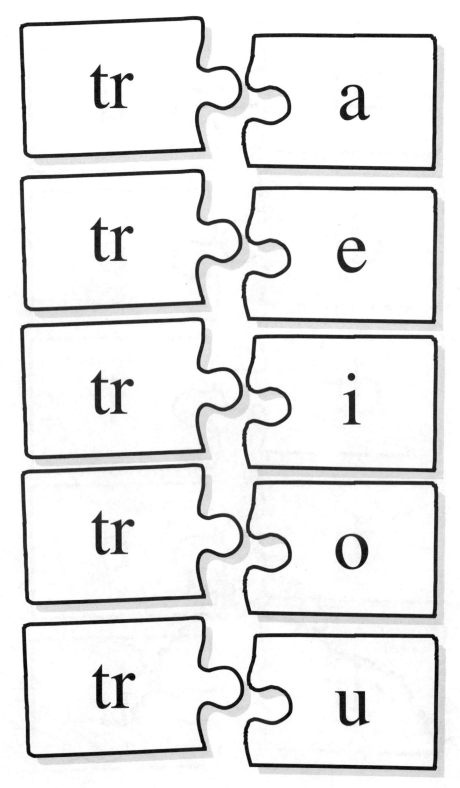

42

## CONSONANT BLENDS

_____
Name

INSTRUCTIONS:
Fill in the letter maze at the beginning of each row.
Then circle each picture that begins with the R blend
sound.

43

CONSONANT BLENDS

Name

INSTRUCTIONS:
When we put pieces to a puzzle together they make pictures. When we put sounds together they make words. Remember when we have an R with another letter their sounds blend together.

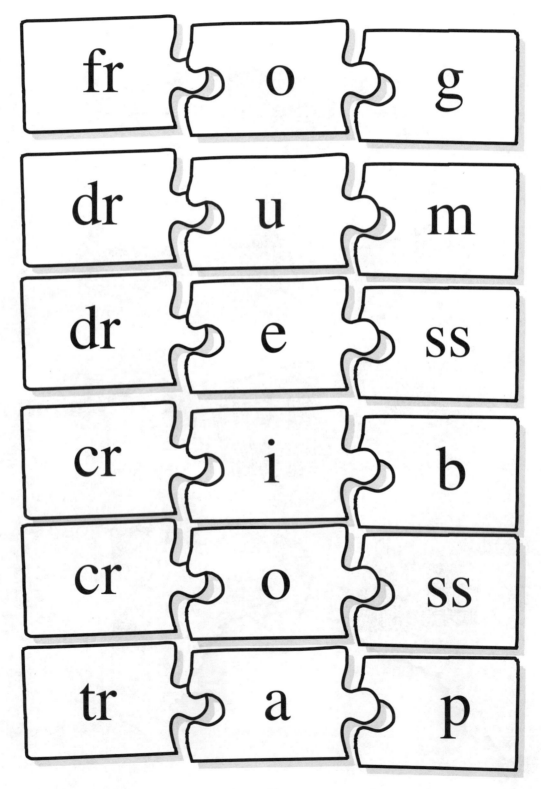

## CONSONANT BLENDS

INSTRUCTIONS:
Read up and down the word columns which feature words from a book you will soon be reading about Alfred the King.

 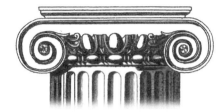 

| | | |
|---|---|---|
| brash | brag | |
| trek | fret | North |
| press | brick | push |
| intrepid | prongs | send |
| grab | prod | who |
| crush | afresh | into |
| trap | abet | |

# CONSONANT BLENDS

INSTRUCTIONS:
Color the presents that have pictures that begin with an R blend (BR, CR, DR, FR, GR, PR, TR, WR)

CONSONANT BLENDS

Name

INSTRUCTIONS:
Match the R blend words on the left with the pictures on the right.

frog

crib

dress

brick

crab

**CONSONANT BLENDS**

_____
Name

INSTRUCTIONS:
In some words the letter L comes after another letter like in *black*. To say these words you blend the sound of the first letter with the sound of L. Circle the L blend at the beginning of each word and read aloud.

| | | |
|---|---|---|
| block | bless | slam |
| black | clip | slip |
| flag | clap | flip |
| glad | clock | flat |
| plan | cling | glut |
| bliss | clang | glass |

CONSONANT BLENDS

INSTRUCTIONS:
Follow the mazes for the L blends, then make them on your own.

*bl*

*bl*

*clang*

*clock*

*black*

# CONSONANT BLENDS

Name

INSTRUCTIONS:
Color the boxes green that have pictures that begin with an L blend (GL, PL, CL, SL)

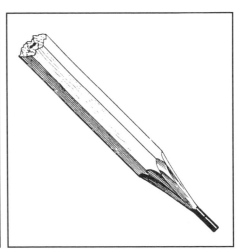

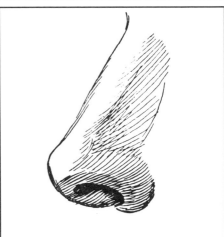

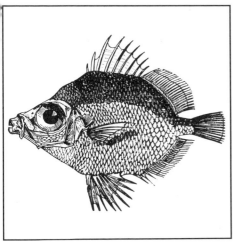

## CONSONANT BLENDS

Name

INSTRUCTIONS:
Say the blend on the left with the sound on the right.

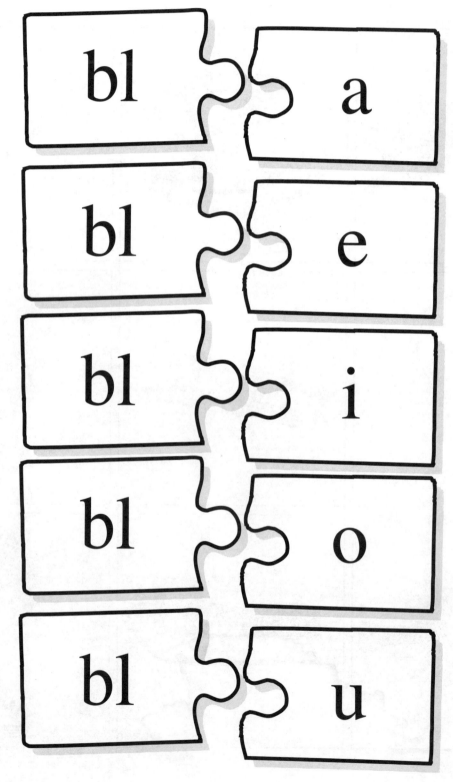

52

## CONSONANT BLENDS

Name

**INSTRUCTIONS:**
Say the blend on the left with the sound on the right.

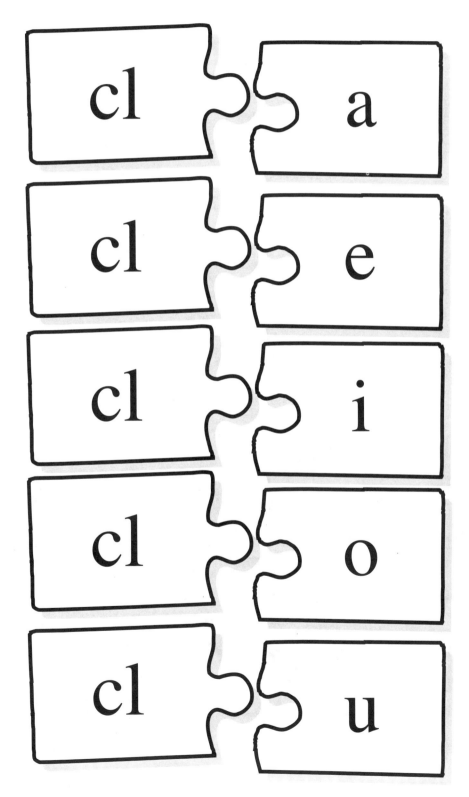

cl — a

cl — e

cl — i

cl — o

cl — u

CONSONANT BLENDS

Name
*Reading*

INSTRUCTIONS:
Say the blend on the left with the sound on the right.

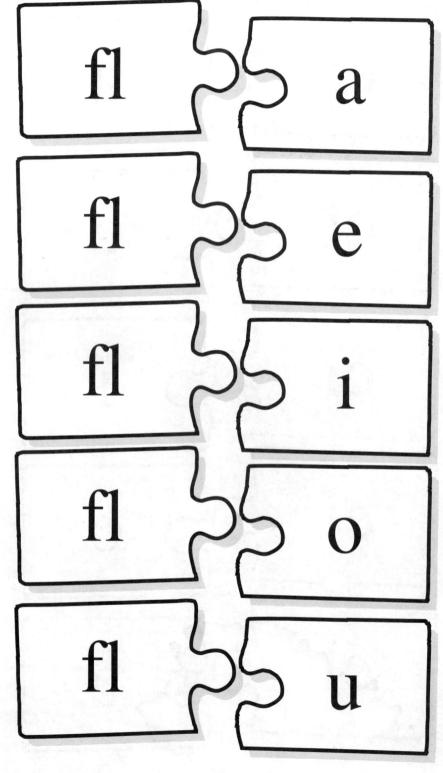

# CONSONANT BLENDS

Name

INSTRUCTIONS:
Say the blend on the left with the sound on the right.

## CONSONANT BLENDS

Name

INSTRUCTIONS:
Fill in the letter maze at the beginning of each row.
Then circle each picture that begins with the L blend sound.

## CONSONANT BLENDS

INSTRUCTIONS:
Read the words below by piecing the individual sounds together.

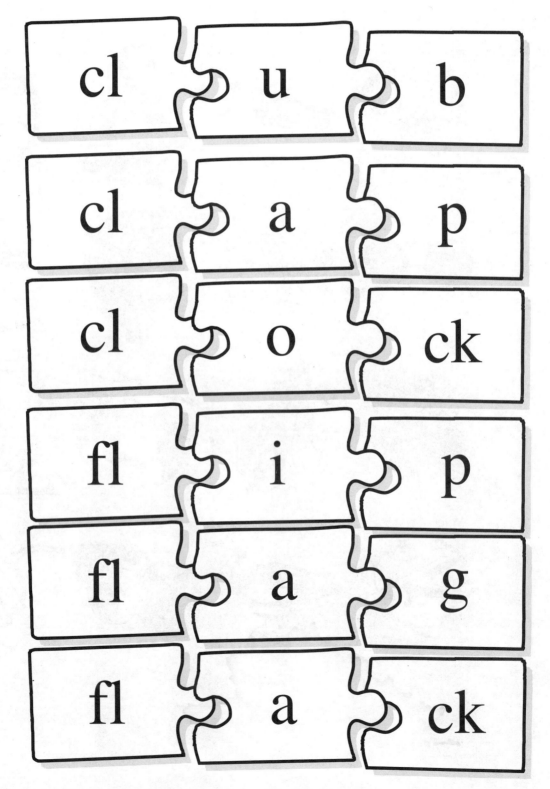

REVIEW

Name

INSTRUCTIONS:
Mount the circle below on cardstock then place a brass fastner through the circle on the next page and this circle to create a color blending wheel.

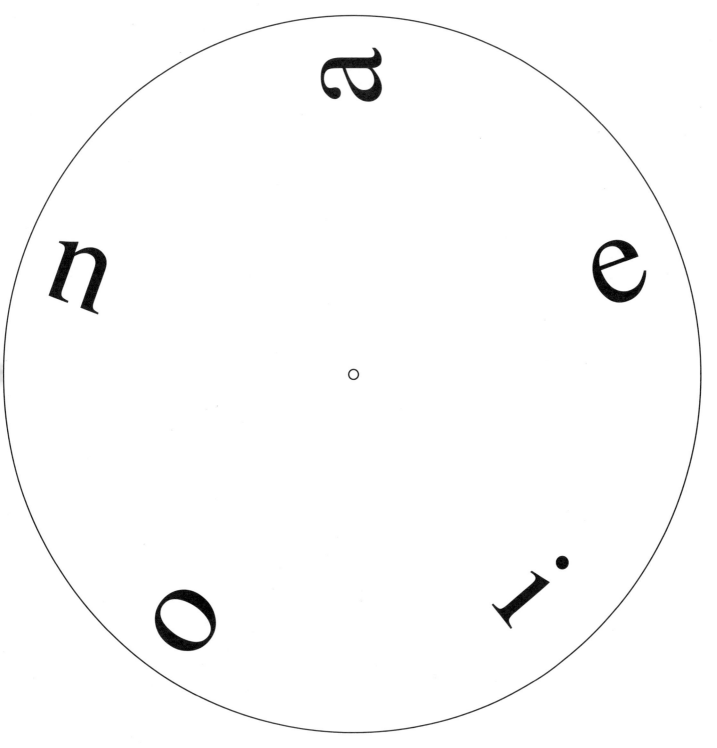

REVIEW

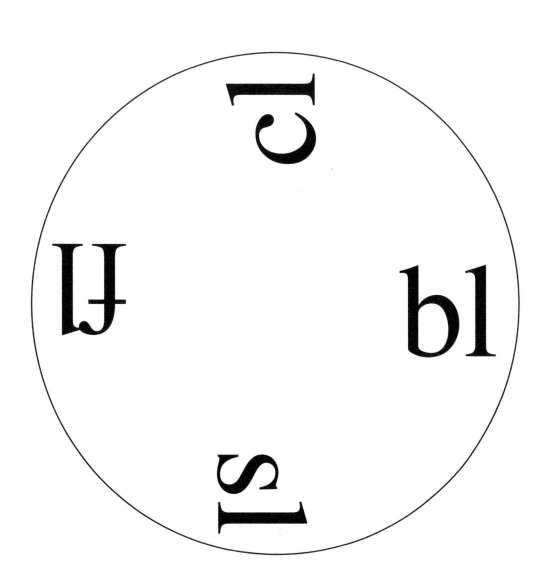

## Consonant Blends

INSTRUCTIONS:
Match the blend words on the left with the pictures on the right.

clock

dress

crab

sled

flag

## CONSONANT BLENDS

_____
Name

INSTRUCTIONS:

After reading the book *Alfred the King*, connect the two ends of the strips below to make a crown. The design is based on a sculpture honoring Alfred's birthplace in Wantage, England.

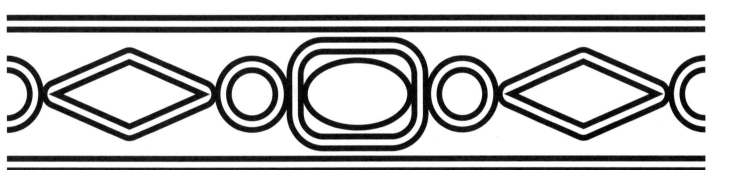

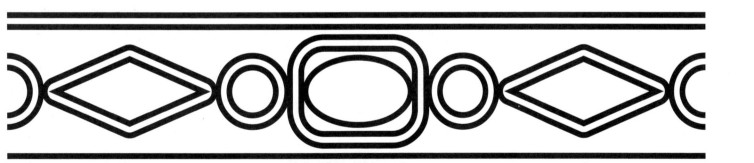

## CONSONANT BLENDS

Name

INSTRUCTIONS:
In some words the S comes before another letter like in the word *stop*. To say these words you blend the sound of S with the sound of the letter that comes after it. Circle the blend at the beginning of each word.

stop      skip      spin

stuff     scat      swim

stick     scan      swam

skin      smell     swing

          snug

75

CONSONANT BLENDS

INSTRUCTIONS:
Complete the mazes for these S family blends.

sc   sk   sm   sn

sp   st   sw   scr

st   sw   scr   squ

str   spr   spl

shr

## CONSONANT BLENDS

Name

INSTRUCTIONS:
Fill in the letter maze at the beginning of each row. Then circle each picture that begins with the S blend sound.

## CONSONANT BLENDS

INSTRUCTIONS:
Say the blend on the left with the sound on the right.

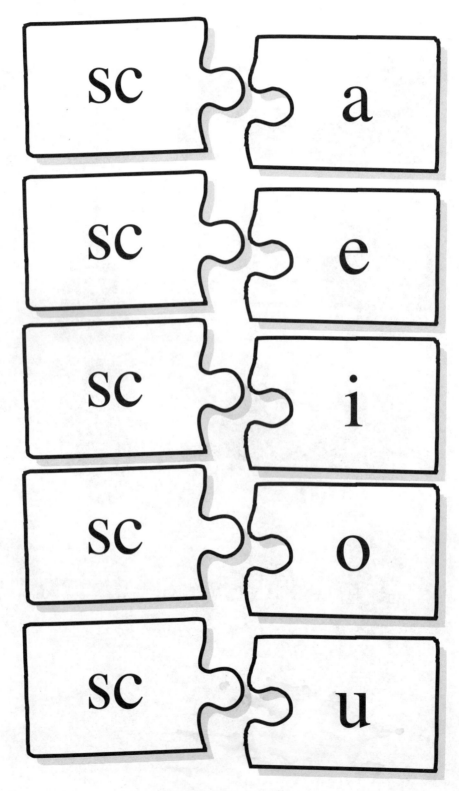

sc — a

sc — e

sc — i

sc — o

sc — u

# CONSONANT BLENDS

Name

INSTRUCTIONS:
Say the blend on the left with the sound on the right.

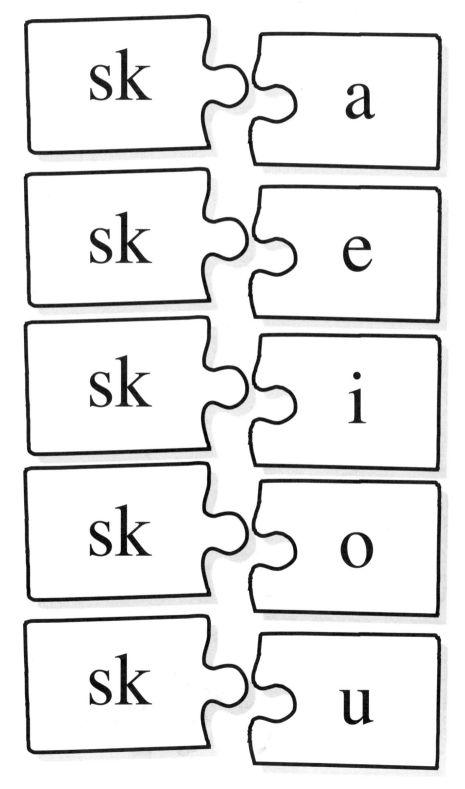

| | |
|---|---|
| sk | a |
| sk | e |
| sk | i |
| sk | o |
| sk | u |

CONSONANT BLENDS

INSTRUCTIONS:
Say the blend on the left with the sound on the right.

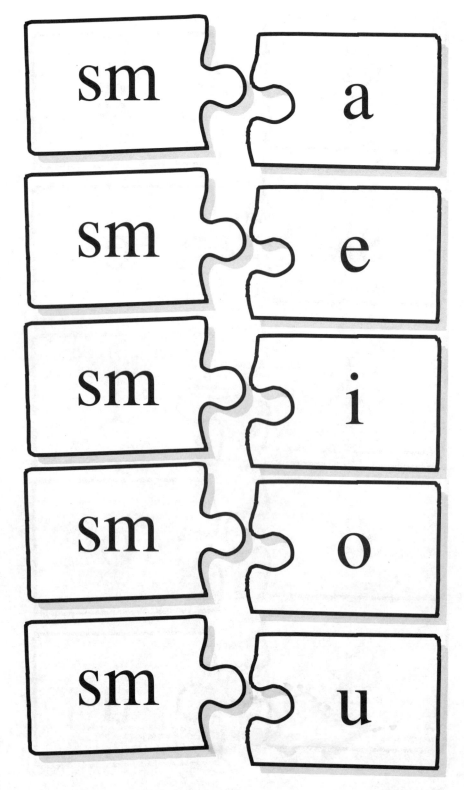

sm      a

sm      e

sm      i

sm      o

sm      u

## CONSONANT BLENDS

INSTRUCTIONS:
Say the blend on the left with the sound on the right.

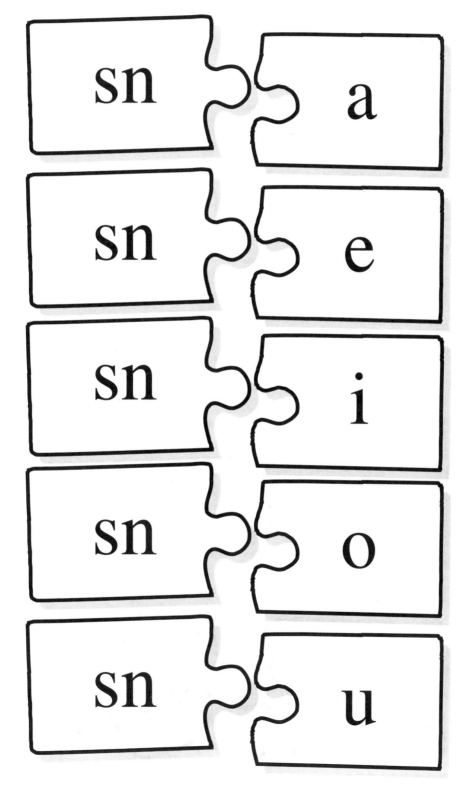

## Consonant Blends

INSTRUCTIONS:
Say the blend on the left with the sound on the right.

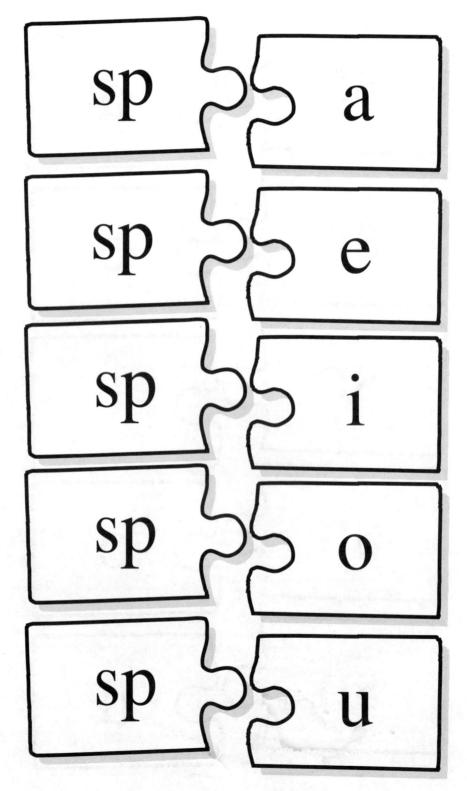

# CONSONANT BLENDS

INSTRUCTIONS:
Say the blend on the left with the sound on the right.

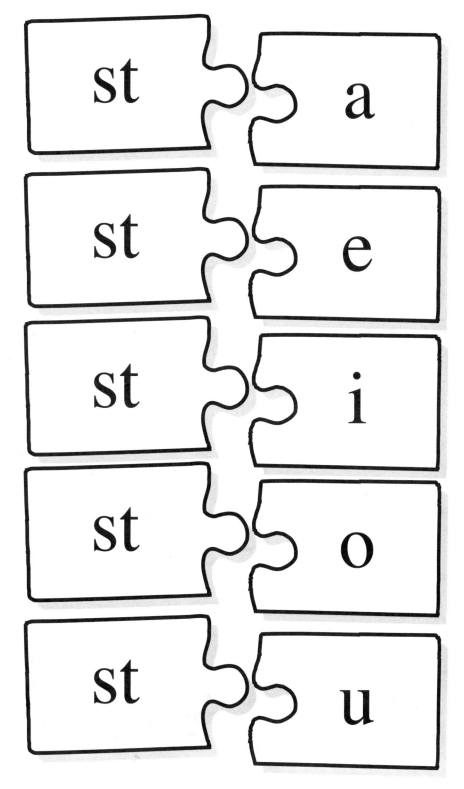

st — a

st — e

st — i

st — o

st — u

83

## CONSONANT BLENDS

INSTRUCTIONS:
Say the blend on the left with the sound on the right.

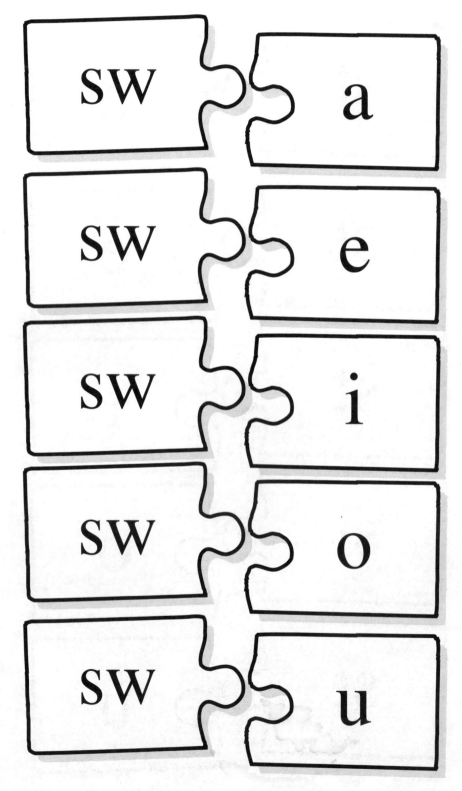

sw    a

sw    e

sw    i

sw    o

sw    u

# CONSONANT BLENDS

INSTRUCTIONS:
Read the words below by piecing the individual sounds together.

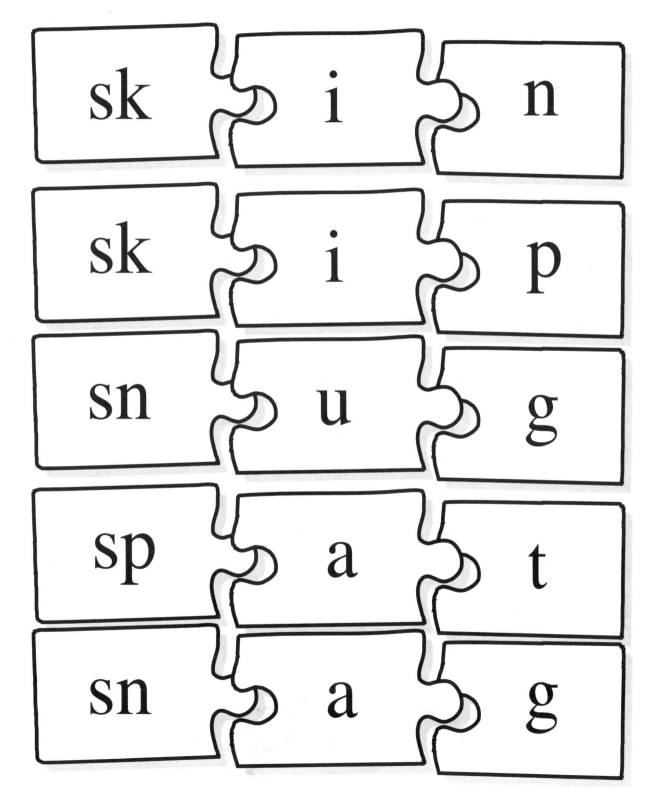

| sk | i | n |
| sk | i | p |
| sn | u | g |
| sp | a | t |
| sn | a | g |

## CONSONANT BLENDS

_____
Name

**INSTRUCTIONS:**
Read the words below by piecing the individual sounds together.

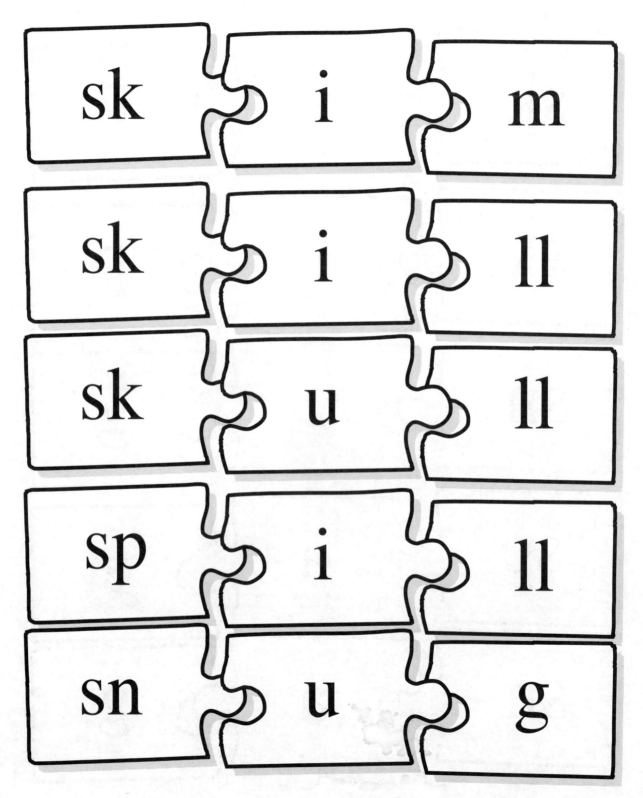

# CONSONANT BLENDS

Name

INSTRUCTIONS:
Copy the S blend words.

snug

scan

smell

stop

scat

swim

## CONSONANT BLENDS

Name

INSTRUCTIONS:
Some beginning consonant blends have three letters (SCR, SQU, STR, SPR, SPL, SHR, SCH). Read the words below by piecing the individual sounds together.

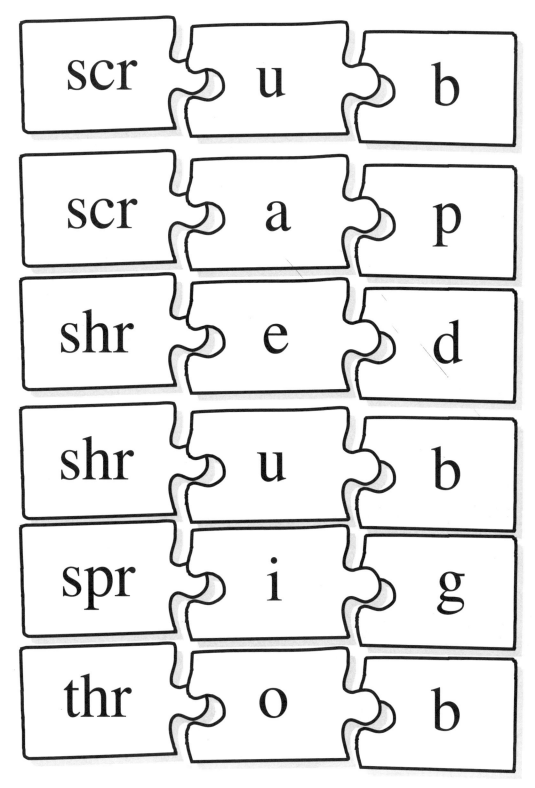

## CONSONANT BLENDS

INSTRUCTIONS:
Complete the mazes below then copy the S blend words.

squall

scrap

spring

throb

strong

shrub

REVIEW

Name

INSTRUCTIONS:
Fill in the letter maze at the beginning of each row. Then circle each picture that begins with the corresponding beginning consonant blend.

*bl*

*gl*

*cr*

*dr*

Name

# REVIEW

INSTRUCTIONS:
Fill in the letter maze at the beginning of each row. Then circle each picture that begins with the corresponding beginning consonant blend.

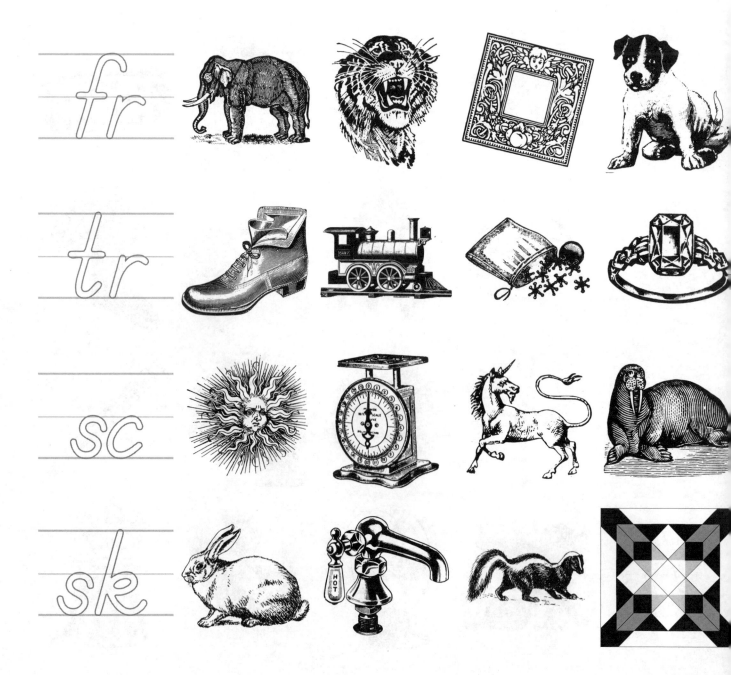

Name

**REVIEW**

brush

bricks

crib

drums

skull

## CONSONANT BLENDS

Name

INSTRUCTIONS:
Read the words below by piecing the individual sounds together.

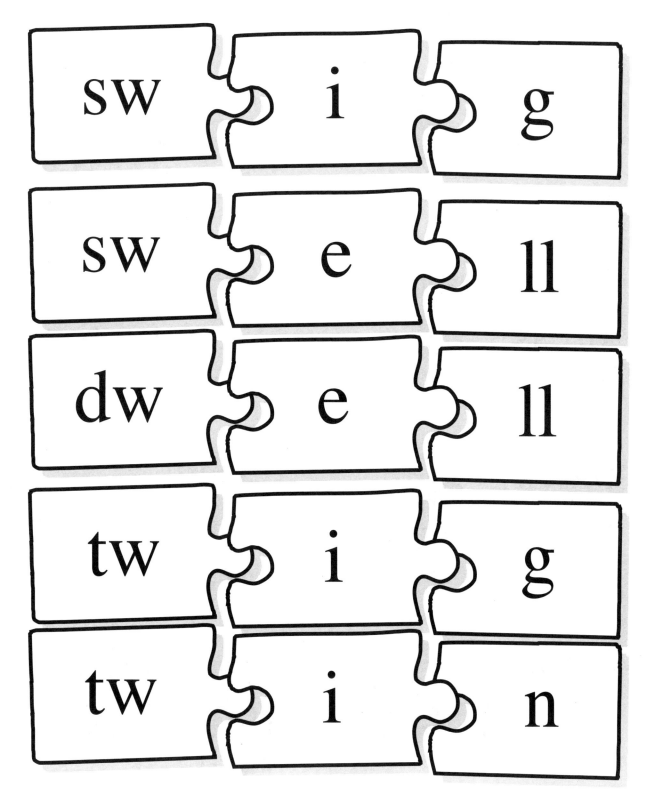

| sw | i | g |
| sw | e | ll |
| dw | e | ll |
| tw | i | g |
| tw | i | n |

Name

## REVIEW

INSTRUCTIONS:
Circle the correct word for each picture.

snag
frog
smog

frog
drum
trap

drip
dress
grass

crab
flag
slip

block
clock
flock

sled
slick
slat

grim
crab
crib

plug
drug
shrug

MY CLARA

INSTRUCTIONS:
Color the trunk of the tree and the bird. Then paste torn green tissue paper on the page to form the leaves of the tree.

## CONSONANT BLENDS

Name

INSTRUCTIONS:
At the end of some words two letters appear together. To say these words, sound the sounds together. Circle the blend at the end of each word (ST, SK, ND, NK, NT, MP).

du(st)        mask        pump

desk        nest        crank

risk        hand        plant

fist        bank        skunk

task        band        sink

CONSONANT BLENDS

Name

INSTRUCTIONS:
Complete the mazes below.

dust     st

damp     mp

risk     sk

hand     nd

bank     nk

mint     nt

# THE GRAND CAT

INSTRUCTIONS:
Cut out the pictures on the right. Glue them onto the blocks on the left, in the order they occurred in the story.

Name

# THE GRAND CAT

INSTRUCTIONS:
Make a windmill.

SUPPLIES:
*Square sheet of paper*
*Brass fastener*
*Milk carton*
*Paints or markers*

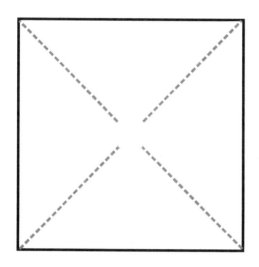
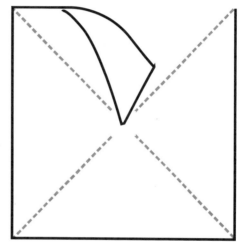

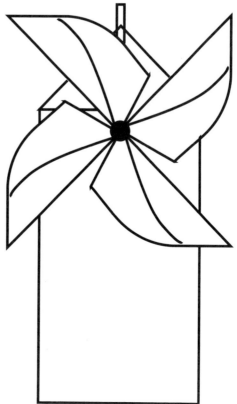

# Vowel + R

Name

I N S T R U C T I O N S :
Read the words below by piecing the individual sounds together.

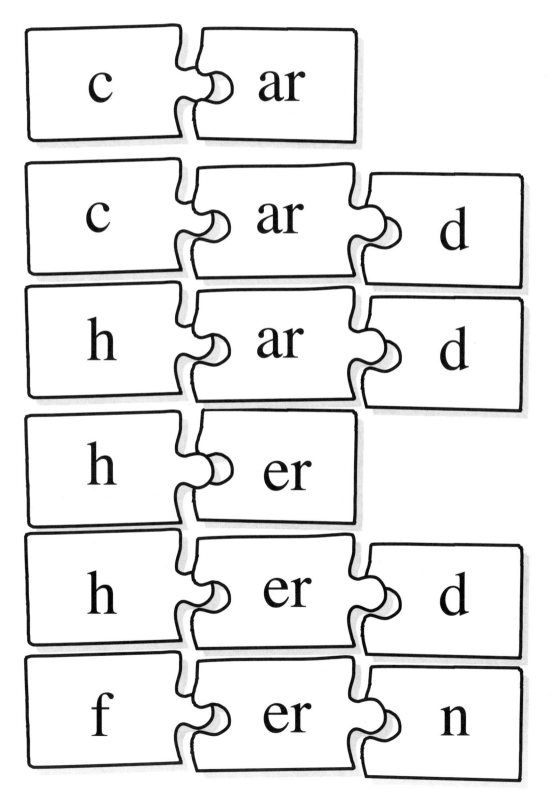

# VOWEL + R

Name

INSTRUCTIONS:
Read the words below by piecing the individual sounds together.

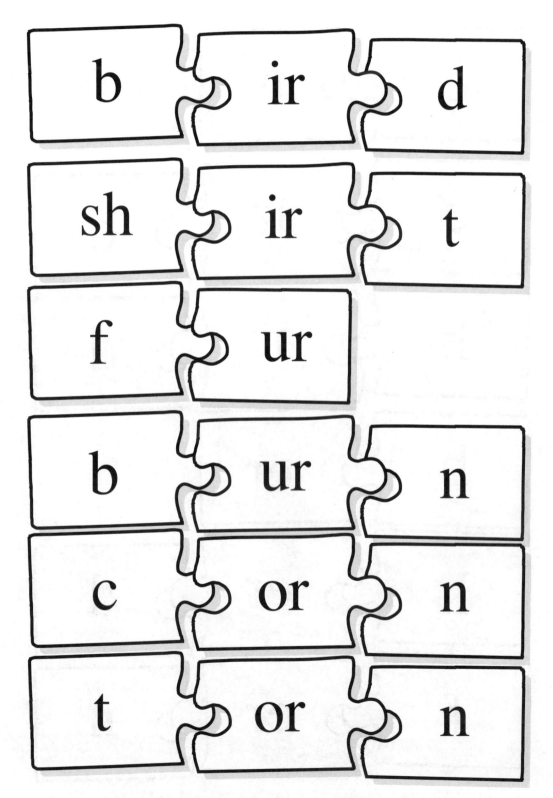

| b | ir | d |
| sh | ir | t |
| f | ur | |
| b | ur | n |
| c | or | n |
| t | or | n |

TEST

Name

INSTRUCTIONS:
Circle the beginning blend for the pictures in the first block, the correct vowel + R words in the second block and the ending blends in the third block.

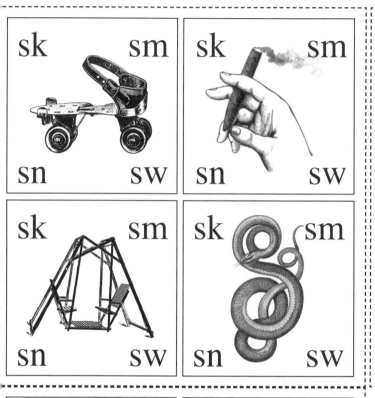

| | | |
|---|---|---|
| sk | | sm |
| sn | | sw |

bird
burn
farm

horn
storm
form

135

## LONG VOWELS

Name

**INSTRUCTIONS:**
Practice making the shapes of the long vowel words below by first drawing within the letter outlines then creating the letter shapes on your own.

bake

wane

save

male

daze

crate

LONG VOWELS

INSTRUCTIONS:
Write out the sentence below.

The mule wore

a yoke.

145

# SPELLING LIST 1

Name

INSTRUCTIONS:
Copy the words on the lines provided.

rope

home

tune

mule

FILL IN THE BLANK:

*A, E, I, O and U usually keep their names, when a silent final _____ is near—as in cute and bike and game.*

LONG VOWELS

INSTRUCTIONS:
When we put the pieces of a puzzle together it makes a picture. When we put letters together they make words.

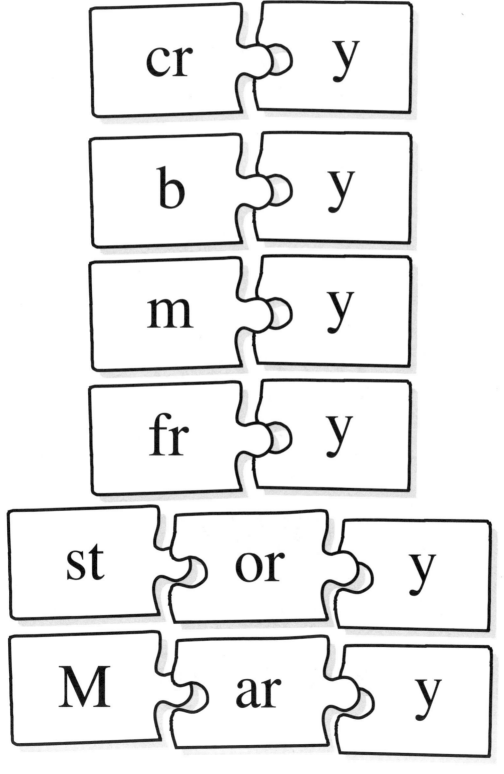

LONG VOWELS

INSTRUCTIONS:
Place a slash between the syllables in the following word

labor

even

began

over

motor

## VOWEL DIGRAPHS

INSTRUCTIONS:
Circle the AI or AY in each word below then draw a line through the silent partner.

| | | |
|---|---|---|
| rain | rail | hay |
| train | sail | may |
| grain | lay | pay |
| brain | play | say |
| mail | pray | tray |
| jail | clay | may |

There are other spellings for the long A sound. The letter A can have a silent partner in I or Y (AI, AY).
*Long A, Long A do you have a friend? Yes sir, I and Y are with me to the end. I takes me on the train;*
*Y likes for me to play. Either way I stay Long A every single day!*

# VOWEL DIGRAPHS

INSTRUCTIONS:
When we put the pieces of a puzzle together it makes a picture. When we put letters together they make words.

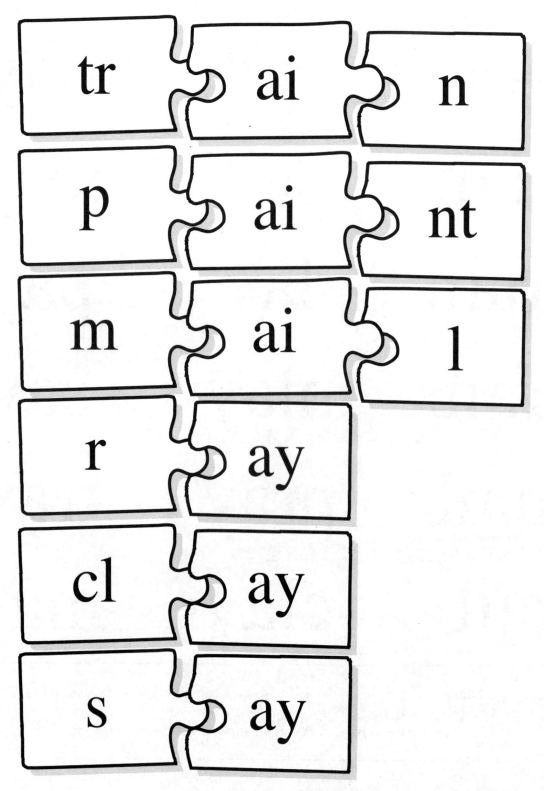

| tr | ai | n |
| p | ai | nt |
| m | ai | l |
| r | ay | |
| cl | ay | |
| s | ay | |

# REVIEW

INSTRUCTIONS
Choose from the following final blends and fill in the
missing letters (ST, SK, ND, NK, NT, MP).

ma___    che___    ve___

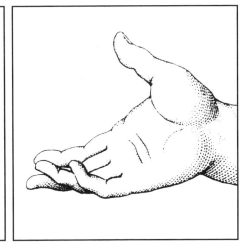

sku___    si___    ha___

VOWEL DIGRAPHS

Name

INSTRUCTIONS:
Copy the words on the lines provided

rain

train

brain

play

hay

clay

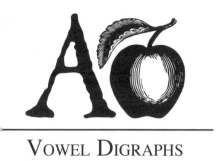

## VOWEL DIGRAPHS

INSTRUCTIONS:
Match the words on the left with the pictures on the right.
There are more words than pictures.

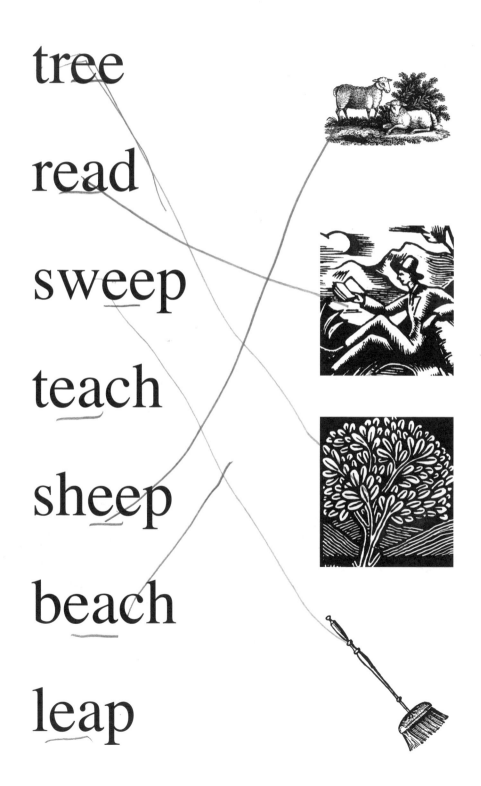

tree

read

sweep

teach

sheep

beach

leap

# REVIEW

INSTRUCTIONS
Choose from the following consonant digraphs and fill in
the missing letters (SH, TH, WH, CH).

ick      ip      eel

air      ell      ale

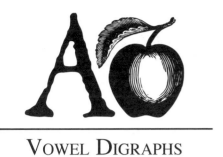

# VOWEL DIGRAPHS

Name

INSTRUCTIONS:
Read up and down the word columns, crossing out the silent partner.

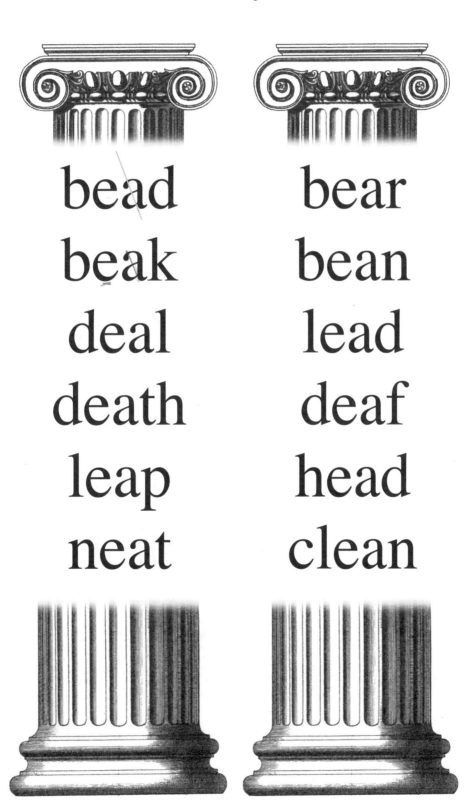

| | |
|---|---|
| bead | bear |
| beak | bean |
| deal | lead |
| death | deaf |
| leap | head |
| neat | clean |

## VOWEL DIGRAPHS

INSTRUCTIONS:
Read up and down the word columns, crossing out the silent partner.

| | |
|---|---|
| read | health |
| bread | wealth |
| dead | steak |
| thread | break |
| dread | lead |
| head | bleak |

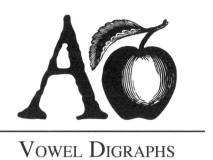

# VOWEL DIGRAPHS

Name

INSTRUCTIONS
Write the correct word under each picture from the following list: LEAF, FEET, QUEEN, LEAP, TRAIN, PRAY, EAR, BEAD, SEAL, HAY, DEER.

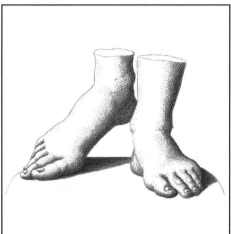

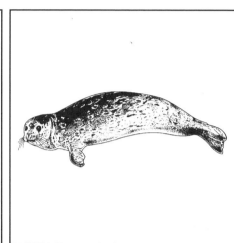

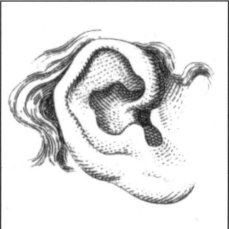

## TEST

INSTRUCTIONS:
Circle the correct answer.

| | | | |
|---|---|---|---|
| long e<br>long i  | long e<br>long i  | long e<br>long i  | long e<br>long i  |

| | | | |
|---|---|---|---|
| not<br>note  | pan<br>pane  | hat<br>hate  | dim<br>dime  |
| can<br>cane  | kit<br>kite  | tub<br>tube  | tap<br>tape  |

| | | |
|---|---|---|
| red<br>read  | sell<br>seal  | card<br>star<br>car  |
| shed<br>sheep  | tred<br>tree  | fork<br>short<br>fort  |

far<br>car<br>jar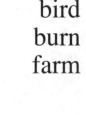

bird<br>burn<br>farm

jar<br>otter<br>jam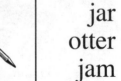

| | |
|---|---|
| chain<br>chip  | neck<br>nail  |
| car<br>chair  | hay<br>hail  |

174

# VOWEL DIGRAPHS

Name

INSTRUCTIONS:
Circle the OA, OW, OE in each word below then draw a line through the silent partner.

| | | |
|---|---|---|
| load | soap | snow |
| loaf | goat | hoe |
| road | coat | toe |
| toad | tow | foe |
| bloat | slow | woe |
| oak | flow | |

The letter O can have a silent partner, oa as in road, OE as in hoe or OW as in row.
*Long O, long O do you have a friend? Yes sir, A, E, and W are with me to the end. A looks like a toad;*
*E tickles my toe; W helps to keeps us straight in a row!*

## VOWEL DIGRAPHS

Name

INSTRUCTIONS:
Copy the sentence on the lines provided

*The toad is on the oak.*

SPELLING LIST 2

Name

INSTRUCTIONS:
Write the words below.

tree

eat

seat

toad

foe

*E A and E E/Operate a partnership/Though one might be silent/Said together they sound just the same/*
*You find them sounding "E"/Like in SEED, FEED, EAT/Their GUARANTEED to always sound like "E"*

## VOWEL DIGRAPHS

INSTRUCTIONS:
Circle the IE in each word below then draw a line through
the silent partner.

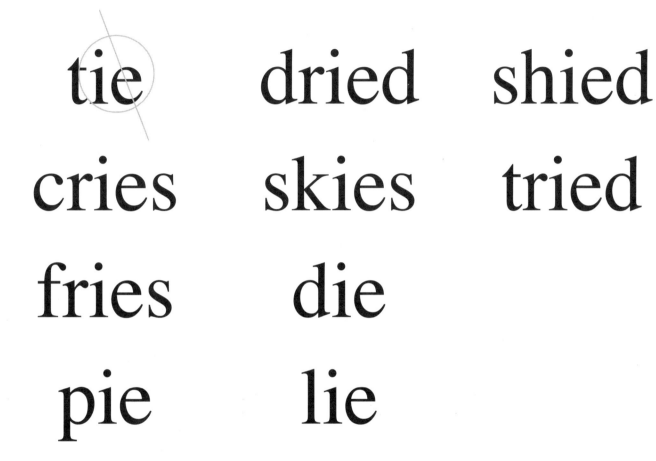

tie    dried    shied

cries    skies    tried

fries    die

pie    lie

The letter I can have a silent partner in the letter E. They work together to make the sound of long I.
*Long I, long I do you have friend? Yes sir, E is with me to the end. Together we can eat a pie;*
*In the past with D we cried. Now with S we are flying in the skies.* (To the tune of Baa, Baa Black Sheep).

Name

## REVIEW

INSTRUCTIONS:
Complete the alphabet dot-to-dot below.

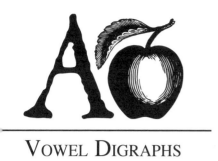

## VOWEL DIGRAPHS

INSTRUCTIONS:
Read up and down the word columns.

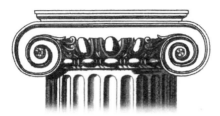
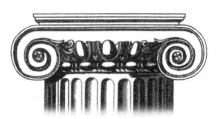

| | | |
|---|---|---|
| bind | sold | scroll |
| kind | cold | roll |
| find | mild | post |
| mind | child | most |
| old | toll | host |
| bold | troll | Christ |

VOWEL DIGRAPHS

Name

INSTRUCTIONS:
Copy the sentence in you best handwriting then color
the picture below.

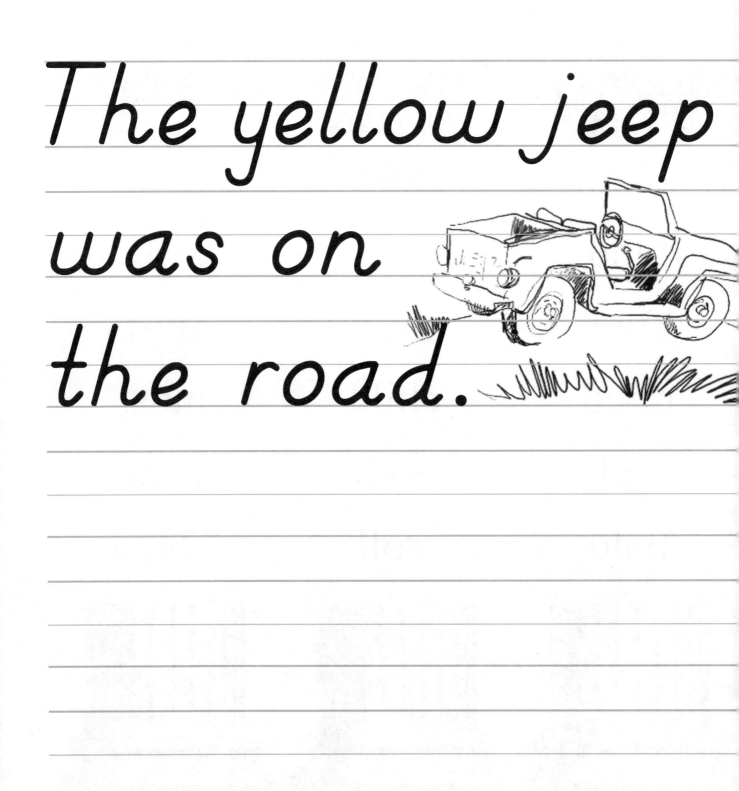

*The yellow jeep was on the road.*

THE
SAILING
SAINT

Name

INSTRUCTIONS:
Copy the sentence then draw a picture to illustrate it.

Brendan was a
sailing saint.

## SPELLING TEST 2

1.

2.

3.

4.

5.

7.

8.

9.

10.

*E A and E E/Operate a partnership/Though one might be silent/Said together they sound just the same/ You find them sounding "E"/Like in SEED, FEED, EAT/Their GUARANTEED to always sound like \_\_\_\_*

A I and letters A Y/Put together make the sound of a LONG \_\_\_\_\_/A I and A Y are in so many words/ Such as PAID, AIDE, SAY, and HAY/ Food the horses eat!

REVIEW

INSTRUCTIONS:
Read up and down the word columns.

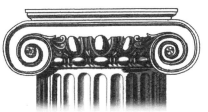  

| | | |
|---|---|---|
| sun | pig | land |
| man | den | let |
| fun | cot | doll |
| red | sick | bill |
| not | rock | tell |
| gun | pack | hit |
| bed | duck | hat |
| top | neck | sand |
| bat | tuck | send |

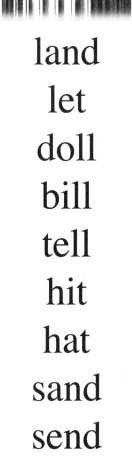

# REVIEW

INSTRUCTIONS:
Read up and down the word columns.

  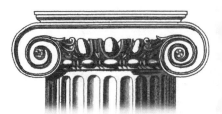

| | | |
|---|---|---|
| dump | desk | shall |
| dent | luck | shut |
| tent | bump | shock |
| nest | win | shut |
| rest | wind | rush |
| hand | wet | mash |
| best | will | dish |
| milk | went | |
| self | shell | |

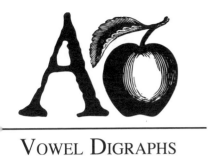

VOWEL DIGRAPHS

Name

INSTRUCTIONS:
Copy the sentence in your best handwriting then draw a picture to illustrate it.

The green tree sways in the breeze.

SPELLING LIST 3

Name

INSTRUCTIONS:
Copy the words below.

beach

heat

roam

float

crow

*E A and E E/Operate a partnership/Though one might be silent/Said together they sound just the same/ You find them sounding "E"/Like in SEED, FEED, EAT/Their GUARANTEED to always sound like "E"*

# REVIEW

d ck

f x

c t

c p

f sh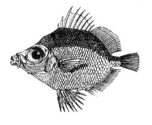

# REVIEW

Worksheet 74B

_______________ Name

*Hearing*
*Writing*

INSTRUCTIONS:
Write the correct letter on each line to complete the word. Then copy the word on the lines provided.

k _ te

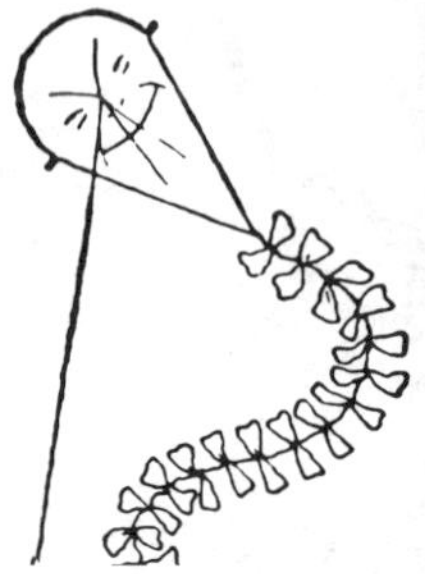

b _ ll

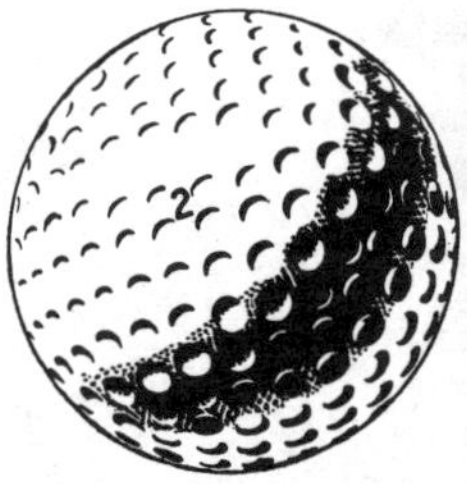

fl _ te

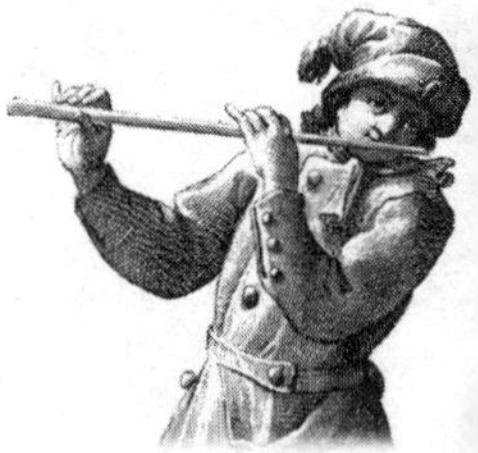

d _ me

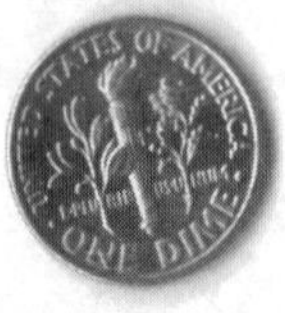

n _ se

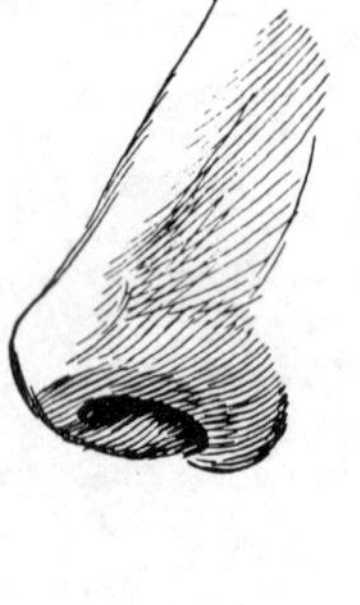

REVIEW

Name

INSTRUCTIONS:
In your best handwriting copy the sentence below then color the picture.

*The red plane
flies in the air.*

## VOWEL DIGRAPHS

Name

INSTRUCTIONS:
Read up and down the word columns.

| home | boat | family |
|------|------|--------|
| loves | sweep | husband |
| hopes | rain | Grandmother |
| bakes | trains | find |
| safe | hears | most |
| Dave | saints | says |
| faith | day | only |
| coat | prays | lives |
| streaks | oaths | Ruth |
| hair | teaches | God |
| glean | wise | Lexi |
| grain | leak | Naomi |
| read | Mommy | |
| beams | Daddy | |

LEXI'S HOPE

INSTRUCTIONS:
Match the words on the left to the pictures on the right.
There are more words than pictures.

bread

tea

pie

cake

butter

wheat

pear

beef

peach

LEXI'S HOPE

_____
Name

INSTRUCTIONS:
Circle the correct answers to the sentences below.

1. Lexi's mother teaches her to _____.

        SKIP        PRINT        BAKE

2. Lexi likes to paint _____.

        HAY        BREAD        FEET

3. Lexi and her Grandmother bake _____.

        BREAD        STONES        BIBLES

4. Daddy teaches Lexi to hope in God's _____.

        TOES        OATH        HAND

5. Lexi likes to read of _____.

        TREES        BUGS        SAINTS

6. God put a _____ in the sky to show his oath.

        BOW        FISH        BEARS

7. Only _____ can make Lexi wise.

        DOGS        GOD        TOAST

LEXI'S HOPE

Worksheet 76C

Name    *Comprehension*

INSTRUCTIONS:
In red crayon circle the things that Lexi painted, in a blue crayon the things she baked, and cross out in a green crayon things that were not in the story.

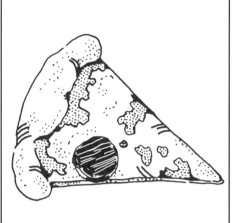

# LEXI'S HOPE

INSTRUCTIONS:
Give students a large piece of finger painting paper and small amounts of finger paint. Have them paint the rainbow from the story, reminding them of its meaning.

Name

# OO

When O is doubled in a word it makes two different sounds as in *moon* and *good*.

INSTRUCTIONS:
Circle the double O in each word.

g**oo**d     bloom     hood

cool     groom     stood

zoo     troop     wood

doom     look     wool

stool     took     moon

soon     brook     tool

*There are twins who* look *exactly the same. They appear as OO, and Double O is their name. When they speak you hear a short or long U; The short one says* good *and the long one says* zoo.

# OO

INSTRUCTIONS:
Circle the squares in blue that have pictures with the double O sound in them.

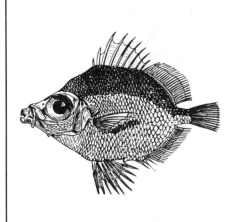

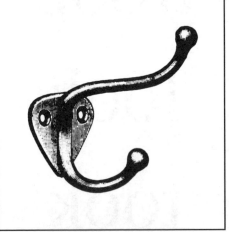
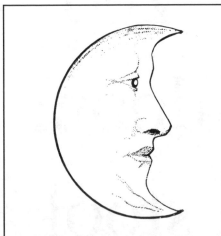

SPELLING TEST 3

A I and letters A Y/Put together make the sound of a LONG _____/A I and A Y are in so many words/
Such as PAID, AIDE, SAY, and HAY/Food the horses eat!

SPELLING TEST 3

---

---

---

---

---

---

---

---

---

---

---

---

---

---

---

---

---

---

---

*E A and E E/Operate a partnership/Though one might be silent/Said together they sound just the same/
You find them sounding "E"/Like in SEED, FEED, EAT/Their GUARANTEED to always sound like \_\_\_\_\_*

INSTRUCTIONS:
When we put the pieces of a puzzle together it makes a picture. When we put letters together they make words.

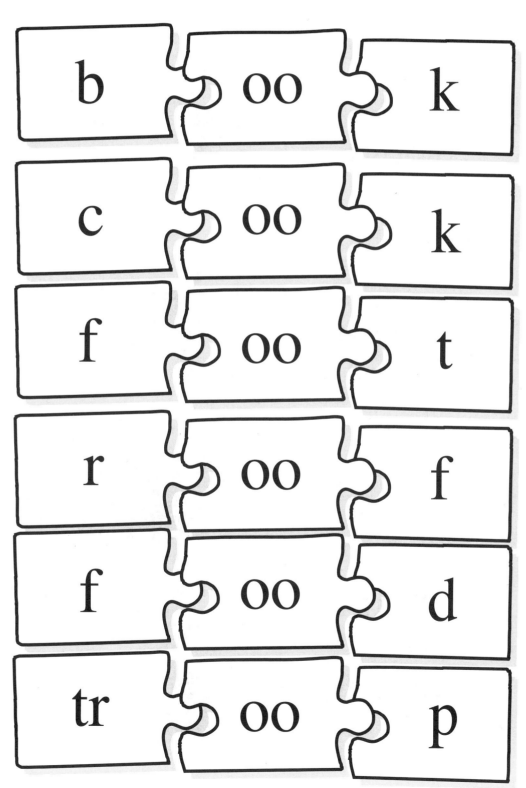

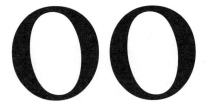

INSTRUCTIONS:
Match the words on the left to the pictures on the right.
There are more words than pictures.

tooth

boot

moose

woad

book

foot

hook

broom

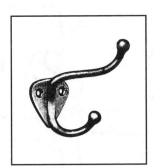

INSTRUCTIONS:
Read up and down the word columns.

| took | spooky | loose |
| tools | looming | roof |
| boot | hood | nook |
| moon | too | good |
| scoop | hoop | mood |
| brook | shoot | |
| cool | loop | |

# ue

The letters UE together make the long U sound that you hear in the word *blue*.

INSTRUCTIONS:

Circle the letter pair UE in each word.

blue          due

true          cue

glue          rue

hue           Sue

---

*Long U, long U do you have a friend? Yes sir, E is with me to the end. We cannot separate;*
*We stick together like* glue. *You could search until you're* blue *and never find a friend so* true!
(To the tune of Baa, Baa Black Sheep)

# ew

The letters EW together make the long U sound that you hear in the word *news*.

INSTRUCTIONS:
Circle the letter pair EW in each word.

news        grew

dew         blew

few         screw

crew        chew

stew

*E and W live very far apart; So when they get together, they catch up on the* news.
*While together, EW says long U to make up words like* grew *and* blew *and* stew.

INSTRUCTIONS:
When we put the pieces of a puzzle together it makes a picture. When we put letters together they make words.

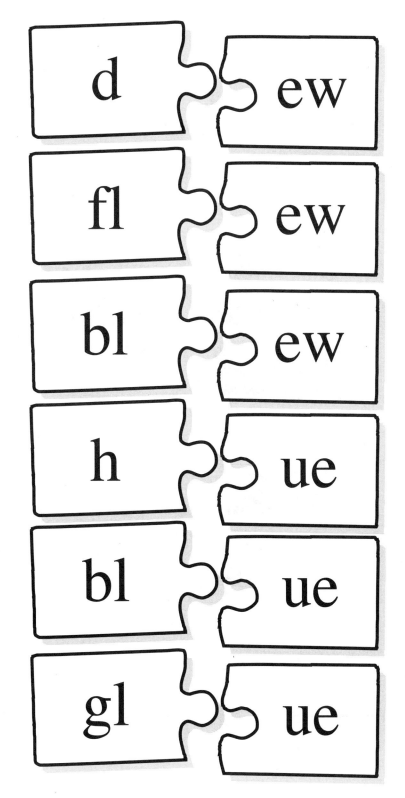

Name

**TEST**

**INSTRUCTIONS:**
Circle the correct answer.

soap
slow

toes
row

hat
hate

dim
dime

window
yellow

boat
bowl

tub
tube

tap
tape

goes
goat

coat
boat

card
star
car

far
car
jar

mow
moon

mate
moose

fork
short
fort

bird
burn
farm

books
bike

door
boot

hum
hook

screw
scrap

## Vowel Digraphs

INSTRUCTIONS:
Read up and down the word columns.

 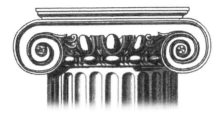 

| | | |
|---|---|---|
| door | behind | croon |
| floor | Mr. | Ka-Doom |
| moor | anything | ray |
| boot | noose | loon |
| scoop | ooze | rue |
| looming | brew | unhooking |
| gloom | rescue | strobe |
| loose | China | swoon |
| doom | goo | self-destruct |
| stoop | spew | mooring |
| troops | swooping | nearby |
| brood | flue | sloop |
| snoop | pursue | anchor |
| beheld | nook | |

RED HOOD

INSTRUCTIONS:
Draw a line to connect the descriptions with the characters in the story.

rom China

ad a Ka-Doom Ray

et the Ka-Doom Ray to self-destruct

sed a hoop to trap his enemy

sed a strobe to blind his enemy

id not escape on a boat

ut a pack by the stream to cool

RED HOOD

INSTRUCTIONS:
Place a check by the correct answers to the questions below.

1. What did the Spy use to fly?

_____ a plane

_____ a bird

_____ a pack on his back

_____ rockets on his feet

2. Who was the evil man?

_____ Red Hood

_____ Sue Woo

_____ Robin Hood

_____ Kung Fu

3. What did the gum do?

_____ It made a big bubble

_____ It ate up the lock

_____ It stuck to the bad man's feet

_____ It cut the rope

4. How did the Spy and the girl get away?

_____ on a rocket

_____ in a jet

_____ on a boat

_____ in the Spy's car

Name

RED HOOD

INSTRUCTIONS:
Circle the correct answers to the sentences below.

. From the back of his car the Spy took out _____.

       FOOD         WOOD         TOOLS

. The pack blew smoke and fire from a scoop and

   soon the Spy _____.

       FLEW         RAN         SAT

. The Spy met a woman by the name of _____.

   BLUE FLEW        SUE WOO        KIM CHEW

. The name of Red Hood's weapon was _____.

   KA-DOOM RAY        GUM GUN        THE ZOOMER

. Place the pictures below in order by placing a

   number under each box

RED HOOD

Worksheet 81D

Name

*Art Activity*

INSTRUCTIONS:
The illustrations for the story *Red Hood* are inspired by Soviet posters of the past that were made for movies and the theater. In the space below create a movie poster for *Red Hood* using only red, white, black and yellow.

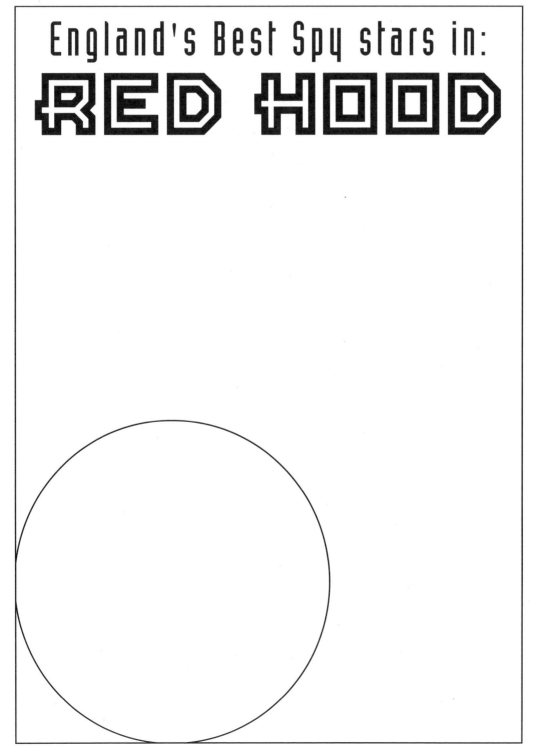

England's Best Spy stars in:

RED HOOD

# oi/oy

INSTRUCTIONS:
Color the boxes blue that have pictures that have the sound of OI or OY.

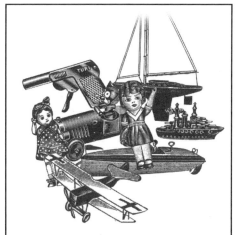

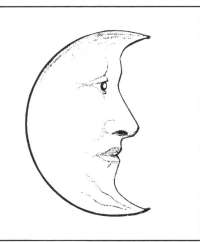

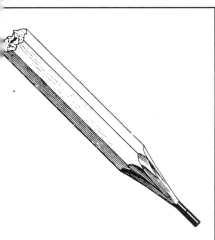

253

# oi/oy

Name

Worksheet 82E
*Seeing*

INSTRUCTIONS:
Circle the "oi" or the "oy" in the words below.

| | | |
|---|---|---|
| boil | spoil | coy |
| coin | toil | soy |
| join | boy | Roy |
| noise | joy | oyster |
| point | toy | |

# oi/oy

INSTRUCTIONS:
Read up and down the word columns.

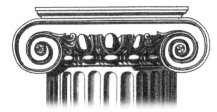

| oil | join | soy |
|-----|------|-----|
| boil | foil | coy |
| toil | point | boys |
| soil | boy | toys |
| coin | toy | joys |
| coil | joy | oyster |

# oi/oy

Name

Worksheet 83B
*Writing*

INSTRUCTIONS:
Copy the OI/OY words below.

boy

joy

toy

noise

spoil

coin

# oi/oy

INSTRUCTIONS:
Match the word on the left to the correct picture on the right. There are more words than pictures.

boys

toil

oysters

boil

foil

toys

coins

257

# oi/oy

Name

INSTRUCTIONS:
Circle the word that completes each sentence.

1. Jan _____ the water to make tea.

        SOIL        BOILS        TOYS

2. The _____ like to play baseball.

        COINS        OYSTERS        BOYS

3. Dad said we were making too much _____ .

        NOISE        HOIST        BOY

4. The _____ is rich and good for plants.

        SOIL        JOY        NOISE

5. We got _____ at the beach.

        VOICE        PAINT        OYSTERS

6. Jack likes the _____ he got on his birthday.

        POINTS        JOY        TOYS

7. Mom wraps the meat in _____ .

        HATS        FOIL        SOY

8. My Dad puts _____ in the car.

        OIL        POINT        VOICE

# oi/oy

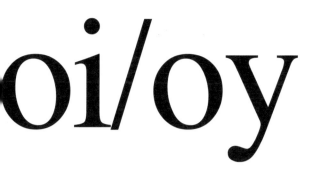

Name

INSTRUCTIONS:
In your best handwriting copy the sentence below then color the picture.

*The boys play with their toys.*

259

# oi/oy

Name

INSTRUCTIONS:
Color the shapes following the guide at the bottom.

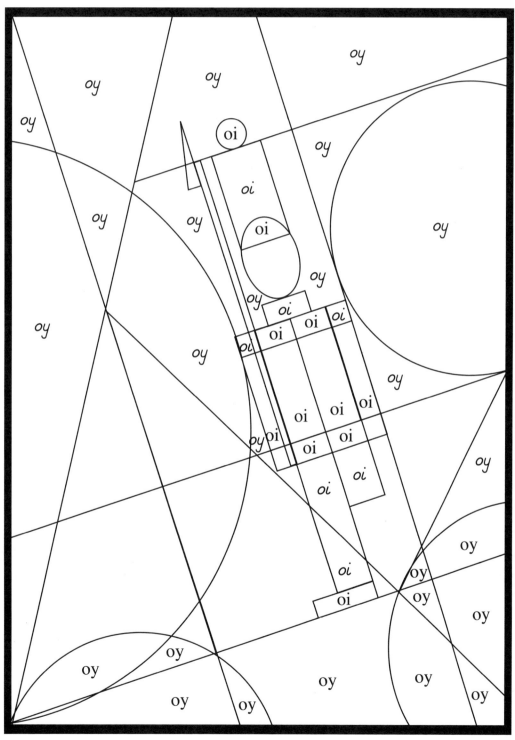

oi = red  oy = blue  *oi* = purple  *oy* = yellow

Name

REVIEW

INSTRUCTIONS
Choose from the following blends and fill in the missing beginning letter pairs for each word (BL, FL, TR, GR, CR, FR, DR). Then copy each word on the lines.

um

apes

ag

og

oom

# REVIEW

**INSTRUCTIONS**

Say each picture. Write the letter that stands for the ending sound of each picture.

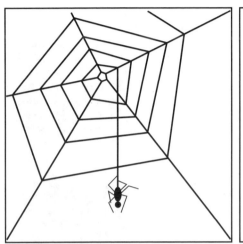

# oi/oy

INSTRUCTIONS:
Read up and down the word columns. Circle those words
that are OI/OY.

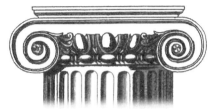  

| | | |
|---|---|---|
| bake | pray | horn |
| boil | boil | coin |
| cake | toys | point |
| coil | hike | park |
| ride | boy | soil |
| rope | joy | join |
| dime | jump | |

SPELLING LIST 4

INSTRUCTIONS:
Copy the OI/OY words below.

oil

coil

coin

soil

join

boy

joy

toy

coy

soy

Name

# REVIEW

INSTRUCTIONS:
Color the circles green that have the sound of IR.

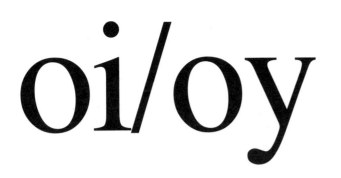

INSTRUCTIONS:
Write the sentence in your best handwriting, then complete
and color the picture.

The boys hoist the toy
into the tree.

Name

# REVIEW

INSTRUCTIONS:
Someone came into the museum and scrambled the letters for the name plates. Match the picture to its mixed-up partner then write out the word beside the picture.

tab

cpu

deb

snu

tac

# oi/oy

**INSTRUCTIONS:**
Read up and down the word columns.

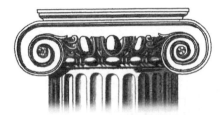
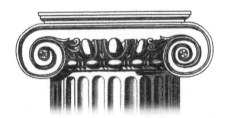

| | | |
|---|---|---|
| Roy | Sir Galahad | marshes |
| moist | King Arthur | quest |
| join | Lord | Holy Grail |
| toying | Sir Bors | fret |
| foil | Hydra | neglecting |
| hoisting | fishing | brutal |
| toiling | digging | loin |
| boiling | pulling | blood |
| joints | looking | spoils |
| spoils | booming | nay |
| choice | thrusting | farewell |
| noise | turning | |

A TALE OF
SIR GALAHAD

INSTRUCTIONS:
After reading *A Tale of Sir Galahad*, circle the
correct answers to the questions below.

1. When Galahad met Roy, the boy was _____.

    SINGING              FISHING              SLEEPING

2. Where did Sir Bors get lost?

    WOODS              MARSHES              HILLS

3. What did King Arthur send his men on a
    quest to find?

    SILVER              MONKS              GRAIL

4. What was living over the hill by Roy?

    CATS              HYDRA              NIX

5. Roy threw a _____ to help Galahad.

    DOG              HAT              NET

6. What did Roy offer Galahad to stay there?

    SPOILS              FOOD              WINE

A TALE OF
SIR GALAHAD

INSTRUCTIONS:
After reading *A Tale of Sir Galahad,* recreate some of the strange fish or perhaps even the hydra using the sand dough receipe below.

SUPPLIES:
Ingredients:
4 cups sand
2 cups cornstarch
1 tbl + 1 tsp Cream of Tartar
3 cups hot water

INSTRUCTIONS:
Mix sand, cornstarch and cream of tartar in large saucepan. Stir in hot water. Cook over medium heat, stirring constantly until water is absorbed and mixture is too stiff to stir. Cool until it can be handled.

Store in airtight container—air dries in a few days

# ou/ow

INSTRUCTIONS:
Color the boxes brown that have pictures that have the sound of OU or OW as in *out*.

273

Worksheet 90B

Name

*Seeing*

# ou/ow

INSTRUCTIONS:
Circle the OU or OW in the words below as in *out* or *cow*

| | | |
|---|---|---|
| out | round | plow |
| house | scout | howl |
| count | how | flower |
| found | down | cow |
| pound | brown | |
| ground | crown | |

# SPELLING TEST 4

Name

1.

2.

3.

4.

5.

6.

7.

8.

9.

10.

INSTRUCTIONS:
Read up and down the word columns. Circle those words that contain OU/OW.

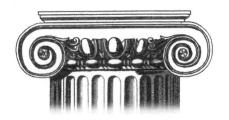

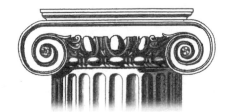

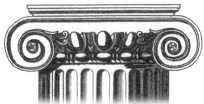

| | | |
|---|---|---|
| our | Howard | browse |
| bound | town | scouting |
| out | crowd | route |
| hour | fallow | prow |
| house | mow | scowl |
| flour | window | dousing |
| count | bows | snout |
| countess | arrows | coward |
| cloudy | flowing | drowsy |
| crouch | grouse | |

ou/ow

INSTRUCTIONS:
Match the word on the left to the correct picture on the right. There are more words than pictures.

couch

flower

house

mouse

mouth

cow

gown

mound

SPELLING LIST 5

INSTRUCTIONS:
Copy the OU/OW words below.

out

house

about

shout

mouse

how

clown

brown

now

flower

The Phonic rule for O U O W / They sound the same though/ The spelling is different
But now you know O U and O W / They make the sound of OW!

HOWARD SAVES
A HOUND

INSTRUCTIONS:
After reading *Howard Saves a Hound*, fill in the circle for the correct answers to the questions below.

1. Why is Howard happy about this hunt?
   - ○ It is the first of the season.
   - ○ It is his first hunt.
   - ○ Howard gets to shoot a bow and arrow.

2. What is Father's job?
   - ○ Count
   - ○ boat man
   - ○ Master of the hounds

3. For what do they hunt that day?
   - ○ fallow
   - ○ deer
   - ○ foxes

4. How did the hounds get across the river?
   - ○ on a log
   - ○ by swimming
   - ○ by boat

5. For what did Father praise Howard?
   - ○ bravery
   - ○ swimming ability
   - ○ wisdom

HOWARD SAVES
A HOUND

INSTRUCTIONS:
Cut out the squares on the right side of the paper. Read each of the "Cause" sentences on the left side of the paper. Glue the "Effect" squares you cut out by its "Cause."

The men see the Countess.

Howard is cold from being in the river.

Howard thinks the hound needs help.

The boat tips when Father gets out.

Father praises Howard.

Father builds a fire.

The men smile.

Howard glows with pride.

A hound falls in the water.

Howard jumps in the water.

281

# ou/ow

INSTRUCTIONS:
Write the sentence in your best handwriting, and color the picture.

The brown mouse runs over the mound.

# HOWARD SAVES A HOUND

INSTRUCTIONS:
Make a pack of hunting hounds using your fingerprints!

SOFT C

INSTRUCTIONS:
Circle the CE or CI in the words below.

cent     cider     race

cell     cinder     rice

center     ace     prince

civil     place     fence

1. If the letter "C" is used before e, i, or y it has the sound of "s."
2. "Ce" at the end of a word has the sound of "S."
3. "Ce" directly after a vowel tells us the vowel is long.
4. "Ci" or "cy" says "si."

ce=se     ci=si     cy=si

# SOFT C

INSTRUCTIONS:
Color the boxes purple that have pictures that have the sound of soft C in either the beginning, middle or the end of the word.

SOFT C

INSTRUCTIONS:
Read up and down the word columns.

| cent | lace | price |
| center | ice | fence |
| cell | spice | since |
| ace | rice | cycle |

SOFT C

Name

INSTRUCTIONS:
In your best handwriting copy the sentence below, then illustrate it.

*The mice prance on the fence.*

SOFT C

Name

INSTRUCTIONS:
Match the word on the left to the correct picture
on the right. There are more words than pictures.

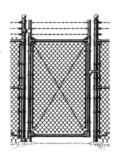

lace

ice cream

mice

pencil

prince

fence

rice

SPELLING TEST 5

1. _____

2. _____

3. _____

4. _____

5. _____

6. _____

7. _____

8. _____

9. _____

10. _____

The Phonic rule for O U O W / They sound the same though/ The spelling is different
But now you know O U and O W/ They make the sound of _____!

## Soft C

Name

INSTRUCTIONS:
Circle the word that completes each sentence.

1. The _____ wore a crown.

        PRINCE        PEACE        SPACE

2. The _____ like cheese.

        MICE        TWICE        SPACE

3. I want a _____ of pie.

        PIECE        PENCIL        RACE

4. The boys ran in a _____ .

        RICE        LACE        RACE

5. Jan likes _____ in her drink.

        ICE        MICE        FACE

6. Jim ate a _____ of an apple.

        CENT        DANCE        SLICE

7. Brandon writes with a _____ .

        CENT        CIGAR        PENCIL

8. The children went to the _____ to see the animals.

        PEACE        CIRCUS        PRICE

SPELLING LIST 6

INSTRUCTIONS:
Copy the soft C words below.

mice

race

cent

ice

face

nice

mince

space

dance

price

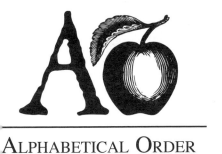

ALPHABETICAL ORDER

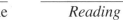
Name

INSTRUCTIONS:
Place the following words in alphabetical order. When you are alphabetizing words and they begin with the same letter, you must look at the second letter to put them in order.

A B C D E F G H I J K L M N O P Q R S T U V W X Y Z

cent  nice  ice  face

1. _____

2. _____

3. _____

4. _____

mince  fence
center  hence

1. _____

2. _____

3. _____

4. _____

pace    piece
dance    mice

1. _____

2. _____

3. _____

4. _____

SOFT C

Name

INSTRUCTIONS:
In your best handwriting copy the
sentence below then color the picture.

*The prince went to France.*

SOFT C

INSTRUCTIONS:
Draw a line from the words on the left to the words on the right which have the same letter pairs in the same positions.

CE=SE  CI=SI  CY=SI

cent                    cyclops

city                    race

lace                    cell

cyclone                 cinder

# REVIEW

Name

Worksheet 100B
*Hearing*
*Writing*

INSTRUCTIONS
Say the name of each picture. Write the correct middle sound for each word.

h t

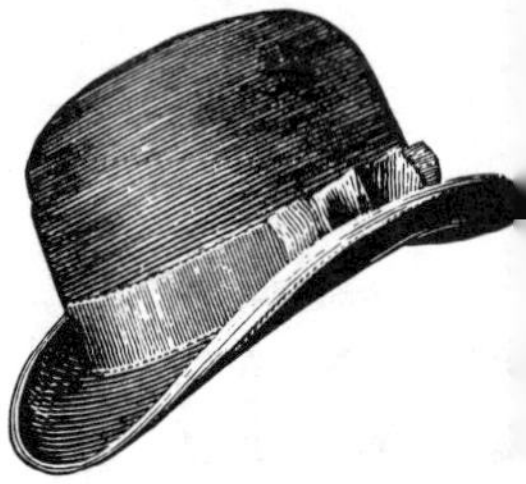

f sh

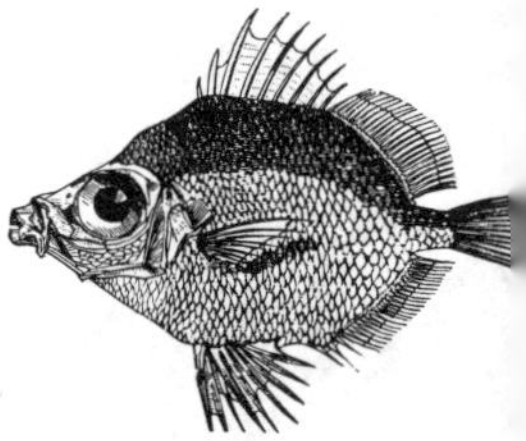

p n

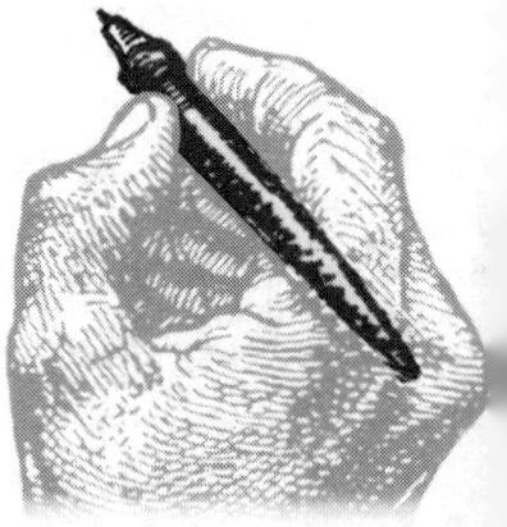

c p

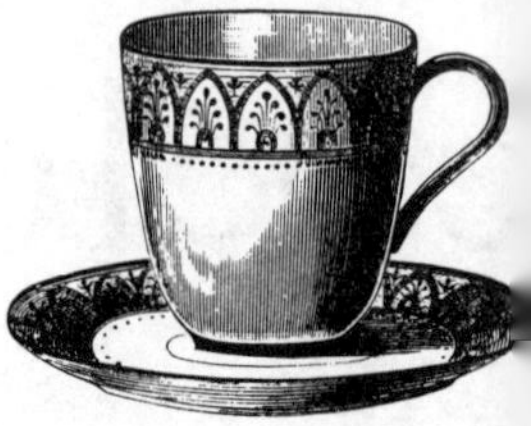

t p

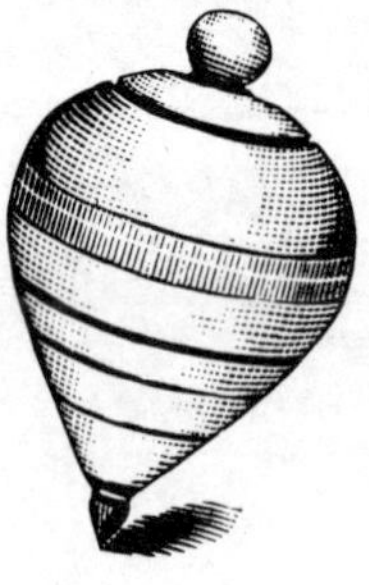

Name

TEST

INSTRUCTIONS:
Circle the correct answer.

toil
toy

oysters
oil

boys
bows

boil
boss

boot
but

glut
goose

moon
moan

ringer
rooster

must
moose

crown
croon

cow
cud

flog
flower

hope
hook

huff
house

miss
mouse

mouth
mine

towel
owl

books
brooks

fence
fast

cigar
sift

broom
loom

poor
pencil

most
mice

last
lace

bear
back

SOFT C

INSTRUCTIONS:
Color the boxes green that have the sound of hard C, color the boxes orange that have the sound of soft C.

cat

lace

cup

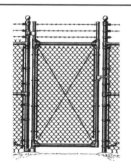

fence

prince

car

dice

cards

mice

## Soft C

INSTRUCTIONS
Write the correct word under each picture from the following list: fence, ice, dice, dance, lace, mice, spaceship, pencil, cent

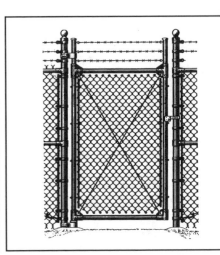

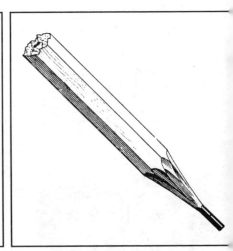

ING

Name _____

INSTRUCTIONS
Write the correct word ending to the words below to match the picture.

box _____

crawl _____

sled _____

rain _____

sow _____

Name     *Hearing*

# REVIEW

INSTRUCTIONS:
Color the boxes orange where you hear the short sound of E and color the boxes yellow where you hear the long sound of E.

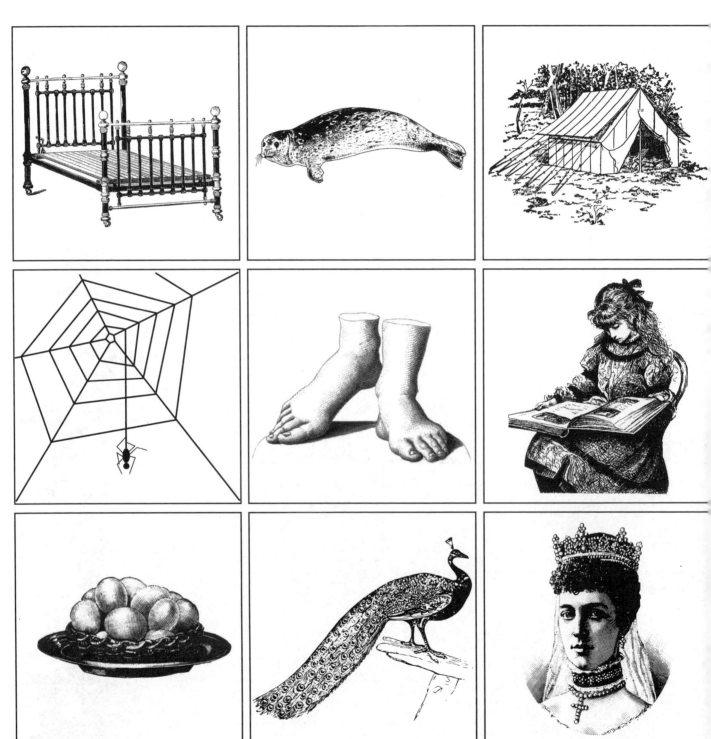

# ou/ow

Name

Worksheet 103A
*Writing*

INSTRUCTIONS:
Circle the OUL in each word and place a backslash through the L. Then copy the sentences in the spaces provided.

should

could

would

Should the prince play cards?

Could the mice roll dice?

Would the cat hold the lace?

## Soft C

INSTRUCTIONS:
Read up and down the word columns.

 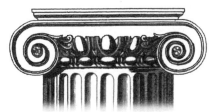 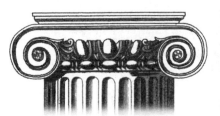

| | | |
|---|---|---|
| wind | voices | straining |
| brisk | piece | bouncing |
| armor | steel | tracing |
| bracing | mail | lacing |
| racing | lace | wincing |
| England | pacing | space |
| prince | since | cease |
| pounce | face | prizes |
| trounce | grace | empty |
| could | price | center |
| would | survive | dancing |
| pope | prancing | hence |
| Rome | female | choice |
| kingdom | Spain | Scotland |
| Elizabeth | slicing | stance |

# SPELLING TEST 6

1.

2.

3.

4.

5.

6.

7.

8.

9.

10.

## SOFT C

Name

INSTRUCTIONS:
Cut out pictures from magazines that have the sound of soft C and use them to create a collage.

QUEEN
OF THE SEA

INSTRUCTIONS:
After reading *Queen of the Sea,* circle the correct answers to the questions below.

1. Who was the queen of the sea?

    QUEEN MARY    QUEEN ELIZABETH    QUEEN ANN

2. Of what land was she queen?

    SPAIN    FRANCE    ENGLAND

3. Who came to attack the queen of the sea?

    THE PRINCE OF SPAIN

    THE DUKE OF WALES

    THE KING OF FRANCE

4. Why did he want to defeat the queen?

    TO GET BACK AT HER

    TO TAKE BACK HIS LAND

    TO GIVE HER LAND A PRINCE WHO WOULD LOVE THE POPE

5. What did the queen promise her men?

    THEY WOULD GET LAND IF THEY WON.

    SHE WOULD STAY WITH THEM.

    SHE WOULD PAY THEM MORE.

6. Which ships were faster?

    ENGLISH    FRENCH    SPANISH

7. Which fleet won the battle?

    ENGLAND    FRANCE    SPAIN

# QUEEN
## OF THE SEA

INSTRUCTIONS:
Make a boat to help the English navy!

Using a half gallon or quart milk carton students can make boats that will actually float. Below is a copy of the English flag that students may color, cut out, and glue to a popsicle stick for the top of their boat. A simple boat plan would be to have students paint their milk carton and poke their popsicle stick flag into the top of the boat. You may wish to give them some ideas and let them try to come up with their own design. They may wish to cut away part of the carton, put rolled up pieces of paper cannons on the deck, or make sails from paper and popsicle sticks. Whatever you do, be sure to test them out on the high seas (bath tub, swimming pool, or lake).

Aw / Au / Al

Name _____

INSTRUCTIONS:
Circle the AW/AU/AL in the words below.

| saw | sauce | wall |
|------|--------|-------|
| jaw | pause | hall |
| paw | cause | tall |
| law | faucet | talk |
| draw | ball | walk |
| yawn | call | stalk |
| fawn | fall | balk |

# Aw / Au / Al

INSTRUCTIONS:
Color the boxes blue where you hear the sound of AW. It may be spelled AU, AW or AL but you only have to listen for the sound AW.

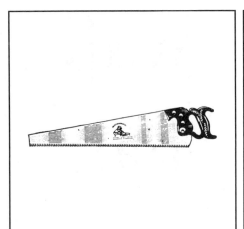

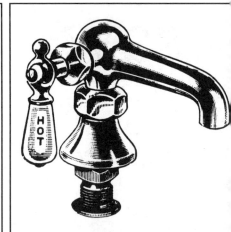

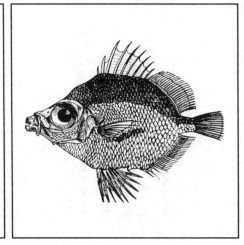

Aw / Au / Al

INSTRUCTIONS:
Read up and down the word columns.

| | | |
|---|---|---|
| saw | lawn | call |
| jaw | yawn | tall |
| paw | haul | talk |
| law | sauce | walk |
| draw | cause | chalk |
| fawn | flaunt | stalk |
| straw | fault | |
| raw | ball | |

**SPELLING LIST 7**

INSTRUCTIONS:
Copy the AW/AU/AL words below.

*ball*

*tall*

*call*

*hall*

*saw*

*paw*

*lawn*

*haul*

*auto*

*cause*

---

The phonic rule BROAD O SOUND/ Is made by A and L "like in CALL"/ And if you see both A and W
It should sound so AWFUL/ Sometimes you'll see A followed by U/ And AUTOMATICALLY know/
That you are using the Phonic rule/ The Phonic Rule BROAD O

Aw / Au / Al

_____
Name

INSTRUCTIONS:
Match the word on the left to the correct picture
on the right. There are more words than pictures.

crawl

ball

fawn

straw

saw

haul

sauce

wall

Aw / Au / Al

INSTRUCTIONS:
Read up and down the word columns.

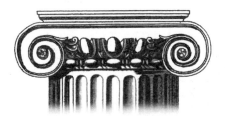  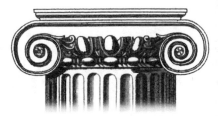

| | | |
|---|---|---|
| awful | lawn | haunt |
| raw | calling | Claudius |
| dawn | small | daunt |
| shawl | also | paunch |
| brawny | balk | Maud |
| drawn | animals | haunches |
| straw | small | yawn |
| draw | because | bawl |
| saw | staunch | jaunt |
| flaws | haul | cawing |
| brawling | Aurelius | fawn |
| claws | squalid | reminding |
| paws | gaunt | |
| jaws | fault | |

**SERVING IN THE SHADOW OF DEATH**

INSTRUCTIONS:
After reading *Serving in the Shadow of Death*, fill in the circle by the correct answers to the questions below.

1. How did the Black Death get its name?
   ○ It came from black spiders.
   ○ There were black spots on the skin.
   ○ It came from drinking black, dirty water.

2. Who died of the Black Death?
   ○ Gwen's father
   ○ Gwen's grandmother
   ○ Gwen's brother

3. What did Gwen and her mother do each day?
   ○ chop firewood
   ○ help the sick
   ○ work in the fields

4. What did Maud say to Gwen and her mother?
   ○ Thank you for your help.
   ○ I wish I could help you.
   ○ Stay away from me.

5. Who was Aurelius?
   ○ a horse
   ○ a buddy of Gwen
   ○ Gwen's uncle

SERVING
IN THE SHADOW
OF DEATH

Name

In the blanks, write the name of the character that is
described by the word or phrase.

# Characters:

## GWEN, MAUD, AND CLAUDIUS

_____ an old man

_____ a small girl

_____ helped the sick

_____ was sick with the Black Death

_____ said mean things to Gwenyth

_____ rode on Aurelius

_____ a lady who lived in a village

_____ had a father die of the Black Death

_____ had a house in the woods

## SILENT CONSONANTS

Name

INSTRUCTIONS:
Circle the KN, GN or WR in the words below, then put a line through the silent partner.

| | | |
|---|---|---|
| knot | gnaw | wrong |
| knee | write | wretch |
| kneel | wring | knife |
| knit | wren | wreath |
| knob | wreck | wrench |
| knock | wrist | gnome |
| gnat | wrote | |

In some words two consonants have one sound, just like the silent partners we already have studied. Look at the examples below.

    kn  as in *knot*—we only hear the sound of n
    gn  as in *gnat*—we only hear the sound of n
    wr as in *write*—we only hear the sound of r

SILENT CONSONANTS

Name

*Hearing*

INSTRUCTIONS:
Circle the correct silent consonant for each picture.

| kn | gn |
|----|----|
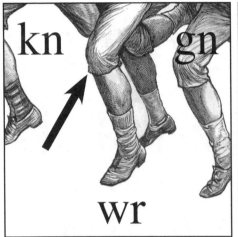
| wr | |

| kn | gn |
|----|----|
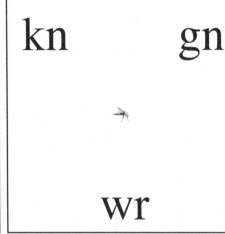
| wr | |

| kn | gn |
|----|----|

| wr | |

| kn | gn |
|----|----|
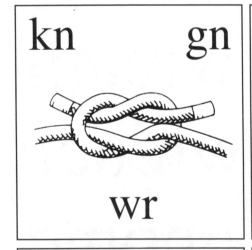
| wr | |

| kn | gn |
|----|----|

| wr | |

| kn | gn |
|----|----|

| wr | |

| kn | gn |
|----|----|

| wr | |

| kn | gn |
|----|----|

| wr | |

| kn | gn |
|----|----|

| wr | |

## SILENT CONSONANTS

Name

INSTRUCTIONS:
Color in the picture below using the key at the bottom of the page.

K = red  G = blue  W = gold

## Silent Consonants

INSTRUCTIONS:
Read up and down the word columns.

| knot | knelt | write |
|------|-------|-------|
| knack | knife | wrong |
| knead | | wretch |
| knee | write | wreath |
| know | wring | wrung |
| known | wren | |
| knock | wrist | gnat |
| knob | wrote | gnaw |

## SILENT CONSONANTS

INSTRUCTIONS:
Circle the GH, MB, LF, LK, or TLE in the words below, then put a line through the silent partner.

si~~gh~~            calf            lamb

night            half            Knight

bright            castle            thumb

light            rustle            comb

fight            dumb            whistle

high            plumb

In some words two consonants have one sound, just like the silent partners we already have studied. Look at the examples below.

lf  as in *calf*—we only hear the sound of F
gh  as in *right*—we only hear the sound of T
mb as in *lamb*—we only hear the sound of M
lk as in *walk*—we only hear the sound of K
tle as in *castle*—we only hear the sound of L

## SILENT CONSONANTS

INSTRUCTIONS:
Circle the correct consonant group for each picture.

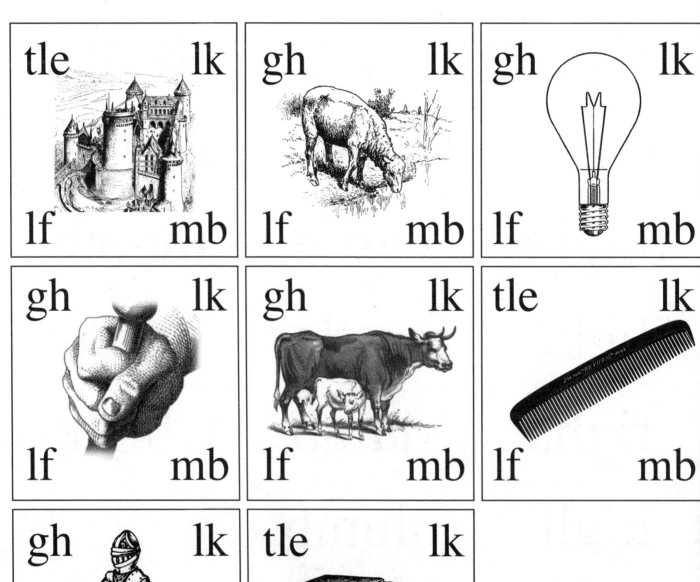

tle      lk

lf      mb

gh      lk

lf      mb

gh      lk

lf      mb

gh      lk

lf      mb

gh      lk

lf      mb

tle      lk

lf      mb

gh      lk

lf      mb

tle      lk

lf      mb

## SILENT CONSONANTS

Name

INSTRUCTIONS:
Match the word on the left to the correct picture on the right.

wrist

calf

lamb

gnat

knot

wreath

knife

comb

knight

knee

331

SILENT CONSONANTS

INSTRUCTIONS:
Read up and down the word columns.

| sigh | high | dumb |
|------|------|------|
| sight | knight | plumb |
| tight | calf | limb |
| night | half | lamb |
| bright | castle | numb |
| fight | hustle | |
| light | bustle | |

## SPELLING TEST 7

1.

2.

3.

4.

5.

6.

7.

8.

9.

10.

ALPHABETICAL ORDER

INSTRUCTIONS:
Place the following words in alphabetical order. When you are alphabetizing words and they begin with the same letter, you must look at the third letter to put them in order.

A B C D E F G H I J K L M N O P Q R S T U V W X Y Z

amb bomb numb
dumb comb

1. _____

2. _____

3. _____

4. _____

5. _____

knee knit knack
knob knot

1. _____

2. _____

3. _____

4. _____

5. _____

## SPELLING LIST 8

Name        *Spelling List*

INSTRUCTIONS:
Copy the silent consonant words below.

knot

knee

gnat

gnaw

write

wrong

sigh

bright

lamb

climb

If as in *calf*—we only hear the sound of _____/ gh as in *right*—we only hear the sound of _____/
mb as in *lamb*—we only hear the sound of _____/ lk as in *walk*—we only hear the sound of _____/
tle as in *castle*—we only hear the sound of _____

SILENT CONSONANTS

Name

INSTRUCTIONS:
Circle the word that completes each sentence.

1. The other sheep had a baby _____ .

    COMB        LAMB        BOMB

2. Pam was _____ a sweater.

    KNOWING        KNEELING        KNITTING

3. The boys are _____ the tree.

    CLIMBING        LAMB        THUMB

4. The girls took a _____ down the path.

    KNIT        KNEE        WALK

5. Jan was _____ her hair.

    COMBING        BOMBING        CLIMBING

6. There is a _____ in the rope.

    CLIMB        KNOT        KNACK

7. I can _____ my own name.

    LAMB        PLUMBING        WRITE

8. Jim uses a _____ to spread his butter.

    KNOW        KNIFE        KNACK

# SILENT CONSONANTS

INSTRUCTIONS:
Cut out pictures from magazines that have silent consonants and use them to create a collage (ex. knight, light, lamb).

SILENT CONSONANTS

_____
Name

INSTRUCTIONS:
Copy the silent consonant words below.

*I ought to have brought the thing I bought.*

SILENT CONSONANTS

Name

INSTRUCTIONS:
Write the sentence in your best handwriting,
then illustrate it.

*The knights fight at the castle.*

## SILENT CONSONANTS

INSTRUCTIONS:
Read up and down the word columns.

| night | high | crumb |
|-------|------|-------|
| slight | straight | numb |
| taught | gnomes | wrench |
| knights | Anne | poem |
| fights | Bradstreet | rime |
| frights | England | fraught |
| sigh | Simon | naught |
| caught | knead | smallpox |
| sight | knock | knoll |
| blight | knack | |

BRIGHT
NIGHT

INSTRUCTIONS:
Read each sentence and decide if it happened in the story.
Circle the sentences that did happen and cross out the
sentences that did not happen.

Anne caught smallpox and was sick.

Anne was in a shipwreck.

Anne went to a far away land.

Anne wrote poems.

Anne was not able to have any children.

Anne was a school teacher.

Anne's house caught on fire.

Anne had faith in God.

Anne's children made a book of her paintings.

Anne was wed when she was sixteen.

BRIGHT
NIGHT

_____
Name

INSTRUCTIONS:
After reading *Bright Night,* fill in the blanks with
the words from the word bank.

1. Where did Anne grow up? _____

2. What did Anne love to do? _____

3. What disease did Anne have?_____

4. Whom did Anne marry? _____

5. To where did Anne go
   with her husband? _____

6. How did Anne and her husband
   get to their new home? _____

7. What did a fire destroy? _____

Word Bank:

HER SON    NEW ENGLAND    HER HOUSE

SIMON BRADSTREET    ENGLAND

WRITE POEMS    ON A SHIP    SMALLPOX

SILENT CONSONANTS

INSTRUCTIONS:
Write the sentence in your best handwriting.

*Anne sought to love God in all she wrote.*

The sun is shining,
  The birds are singing
  And my eyes are waking.
  I think of things I'll do today.
There will be
☐   running and _____,
☐   laughter and _____,
☐   books and _____.

The sun is high,
  My friends are here
  And I am _____.
We plan our day's adventures.
We will
☐   talk and _____,
☐   make and _____,
☐   eat and _____.

The moon is high,
  The stars are shining
  My family is giving thanks.
I thank thee good Lord
For
☐   playmates and _____,
☐   food and _____,
☐   books and _____.
And for your Presence always with me.

Name

# REVIEW

INSTRUCTIONS:
Circle the correct beginning blend for each picture.

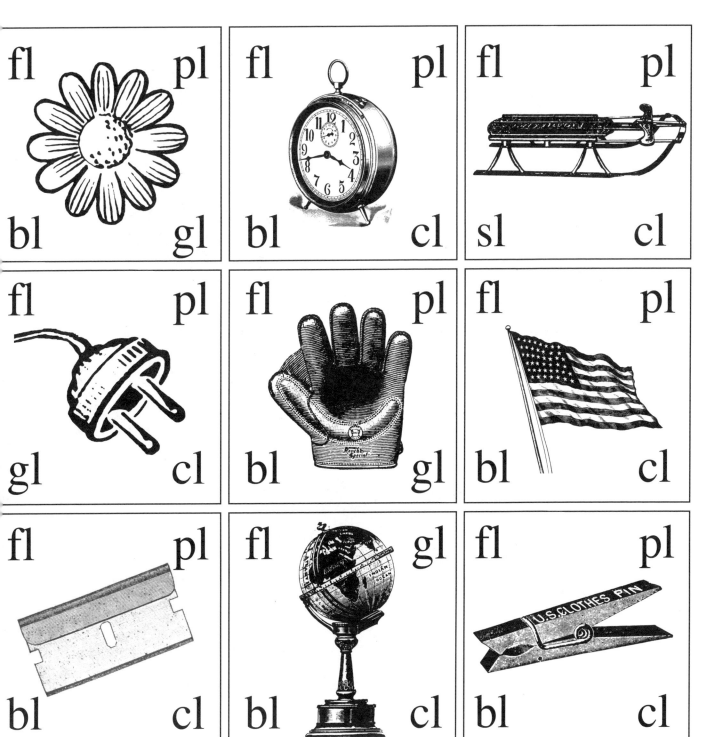

| fl | | pl |
| bl | | gl |

| fl | | pl |
| bl | | cl |

| fl | | pl |
| sl | | cl |

| fl | | pl |
| gl | | cl |

| fl | | pl |
| bl | | gl |

| fl | | pl |
| bl | | cl |

| fl | | pl |
| bl | | cl |

| fl | | gl |
| bl | | cl |

| fl | | pl |
| bl | | cl |

Name

## ALPHABETICAL ORDER

INSTRUCTIONS:
Complete the picture by connecting the dots in alphabetical order.

## SPELLING TEST 8

1.

2.

3.

4.

5.

6.

7.

8.

9.

10.

If as in *calf*—we only hear the sound of _____/   gh as in *right*—we only hear the sound of _____/
mb as in *lamb*—we only hear the sound of _____/   lk as in *walk*—we only hear the sound of _____/
tle as in *castle*—we only hear the sound of _____

J SOUND OF GE/DGE

INSTRUCTIONS:
Match the word on the left to the correct picture on the right. There are more words than pictures.

bridge

hedge

cage

page

judge

fudge

badge

## J SOUND OF GE/DGE

Name

*Hearing*

INSTRUCTIONS:
Color the boxes purple that have pictures that have the sound of J made by the GE/DGE letter combination.

Name

J SOUND OF GE/DGE

INSTRUCTIONS:
Read up and down the word columns.

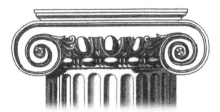

| bridge | badge | edge |
|--------|-------|------|
| hedge | cage | fudge |
| cage | page | ridge |
| page | age | hedge |
| judge | rage | bridge |
| fudge | hinge | |

REVIEW

Name

INSTRUCTIONS
Say each picture. Write AR or ER in to complete each word.

st

c

b n

zipp

hamm

TEST

_____
Name

INSTRUCTIONS
Circle the correct answer.

dice
date

lake
lace

knight
kite

lamp
lamb

price
prince

mate
mice

carpet
castle

camp
comb

face
faucet

saw
seen

judge
jump

brick
bridge

bear
barn

crawl
crab

bait
badge

cage
cape

gnat
gnome

knot
coat

walrus
walnut

face
faucet

saint
sauce

bat
ball

dart
dance

cow
cot

mount
mouth

J SOUND OF GE/DGE

INSTRUCTIONS:
Read up and down the word columns.

| | | |
|---|---|---|
| pledge | challenge | damage |
| diligent | trudge | arrange |
| charge | voyage | intelligent |
| barrage | edge | strange |
| grudge | huge | enrage |
| large | bridge | |
| purge | judge | |

## ALPHABETICAL ORDER

Name

INSTRUCTIONS:
On the lines provided below, write out the entire alphabet in order including both upper and lower case letters.

1. _____

2. _____

3. _____

4. _____

5. _____

6. _____

7. _____

8. _____

9. _____

10. _____

11. _____

12. _____

13. _____

14. _____

15. _____

16. _____

17. _____

18. _____

19. _____

20. _____

21. _____

22. _____

23. _____

24. _____

25. _____

26. _____

_____
Name

J SOUND OF GE/DGE

INSTRUCTIONS:
Circle the word that completes each sentence.

1. The man was trimming his _____ .

         BUDGE         LODGE         HEDGE

2. Travis and Brandon made yummy _____ .

         FUDGE         BRIDGE         RIDGE

3. The bird is in its _____ .

         CAGE         SAGE         WAGE

4. Please turn to the next _____ in your book.

         RAGE         CAGE         PAGE

5. When I paid my bill the man gave me _____ .

         HINGE         CHANGE         PLUNGE

6. The play was on the _____ .

         AGE         STAGE         WAGE

7. We took a walk over the _____ .

         FUDGE         DODGE         BRIDGE

8. The window has a _____ on it.

         HUGE         SMUDGE         AGE

Name    *Art Activity*

## ALPHABETICAL ORDER

INSTRUCTIONS:
Complete the picture by connecting the dots then color.

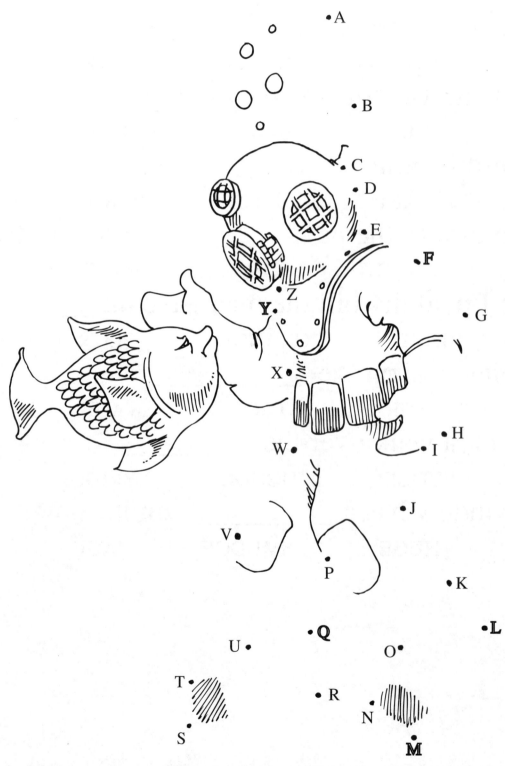

Name

REVIEW

INSTRUCTIONS
Read each word. Circle the vowel pair then write the
sound which the two letters make on the line.

feet _*e*_

leap _____

tree _____

soak _____

sea _____

coat _____

teach _____

feast _____

week _____

sheet _____

tea _____

loaf _____

toes _____

float _____

keep _____

sweet _____

dream _____

fleet _____

coast _____

## J SOUND OF GE/DGE

Name      *Writing*

INSTRUCTIONS:
Write the sentence in your best handwriting.

*The cat does not budge when the boy jumps over the hedge.*

J SOUND OF GE/DGE

INSTRUCTIONS:
Circle the GE or GI in the words below, then read them aloud.

gem        germ        margin

gee        gin        tragic

gel        ginger        urgent

gentle        magic

SPELLING LIST 9

INSTRUCTIONS:
Copy the GE/DGE words below.

cage

page

age

rage

hinge

edge

fudge

ridge

hedge

bridge

# REVIEW

INSTRUCTIONS:
Say each picture. Write the consonant letter needed to
complete each word.

spoo

fo

ench

bir

ence

## J SOUND OF GE/DGE

INSTRUCTIONS:
Read up and down the word columns.

  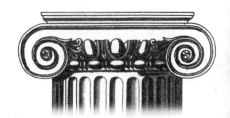

| | | |
|---|---|---|
| pledge | bridge | Marathon |
| diligent | judge | enrage |
| charge | damage | genius |
| barrage | arrange | important |
| grudge | intelligent | preparing |
| large | strange | |
| purge | archer | |
| challenge | army | Cyrus |
| trudge | enemies | very |
| voyage | weapon | body |
| edge | arrow | build |
| huge | battle | two |

J SOUND OF GE/DGE

INSTRUCTIONS:
Write the sentence in your best handwriting.

*I am Cyrus, an archer in the army from the East.*

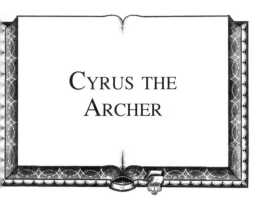

CYRUS THE
ARCHER

INSTRUCTIONS:
After reading *Cyrus the Archer,* circle the correct
answers to the questions below.

1. What is Cyrus' job?

    ARMOR BEARER    MESSENGER    ARCHER

2. What is the main weapon in use by most of
the enemies?

    SWORDS    SPEARS    GUNS

3. What army are they on their way to attack?

    ROME    SPAIN    GREECE

4. What was laid across the boats so the army
could walk on them?

    BRICKS    ROPES    PLANKS

5. How many days did it take for the army to
cross the bridge?

    SEVEN    FIVE    TEN

6. What other problem did the army of the East face
before they began the attack?

    A DESERT    STEEP HILLS    LACK OF FOOD

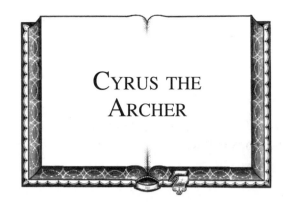

CYRUS THE ARCHER

INSTRUCTIONS:
Build a model bridge.

SUPPLIES:
*A large bucket, pot, or bath tub*
*Paper cups*
*Popsicle sticks*
*Yarn or string*
*Long, thin rocks*
*Mud or clay*
*A sewing pin*

1.  Cut off the tops of the paper cups so that they are only 2" deep.  Pinch two opposite sides of the cups so they take on a boat shape.
2.  With a pin poke a hole on the top edge of the cups about 1/2" down from the top of the cup and near the middle of the boat.  Poke another hole 1/2" down on the opposite side of the cups.
3.  Tape the string or yarn to the pin and thread it through the holes in the cups so that they are tied together side by side.  Knot both ends of the string.
4.  Tie string around the thin rocks and then attach the string to the boats.  These are the rock anchors used to steady the boats in the water.
5.  Lay three popsicle sticks with middles together. These will be the wooden planks for the bridge. Press the mud or clay onto the sticks.  Make enough sets of three so that when placed end to end they will stretch across the row of boats.  Mud will have to dry before the popsicle sticks are placed on top of the boat.
6.  You may wish to photocopy onto card stock the Persian soldiers and animals at the right, then cut them out to place them on the bridge and/or the two banks.
7.  Fill a tub with water and put the bridge in the water.

# REVIEW

Name

INSTRUCTIONS:
Say each picture. Circle whether the vowel sound
is short or long.

long a
short a
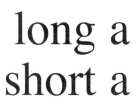

long i
short i

long a
short a

long o
short o

long e
short e

long o
short o

long e
short e

long u
short u
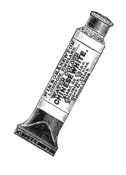

# REVIEW

INSTRUCTIONS
Say each picture. Write CH, SH, TH, or WH to complete each word.

___ell

___umb

___ip

___ale

___ick

TION / SION

TION and SION are pronounced "shun."
INSTRUCTIONS:
Circle the TION or the SION in the words below.

sta(tion)

section

impression

nation

ignition

mission

creation

celebration

decision

motion

vision

confession

portion

division

pension

SPELLING TEST 9

1.

2.

3.

4.

5.

6.

7.

8.

9.

10.

TION / SION

Name

INSTRUCTIONS:
Color the shapes following the guide at the bottom to complete this vacation picture.

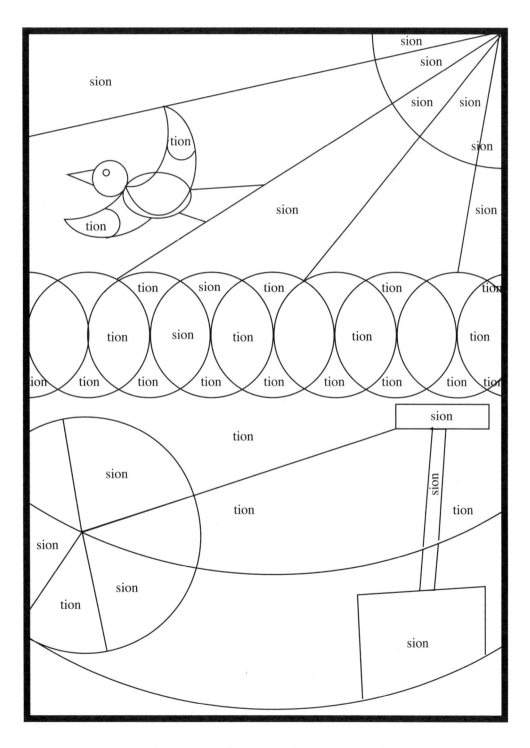

tion = blue    sion = red

## TION / SION

INSTRUCTIONS:
Read up and down the word columns.

| nation | ignition | impression |
|--------|----------|------------|
| station | vision | mission |
| motion | division | session |
| creation | decision | mansion |
| portion | confession | passion |
| section | pension | |

_____  
Name

TION / SION

INSTRUCTIONS:
Circle the word that completes each sentence.

1. My family is going on a summer _____ .

      HESITATION          VACATION          EXPLOSION

2. Tom Edison made many _____ .

      EXPRESSIONS          INVENTIONS          DIVISIONS

3. I sent out many _____ to the party.

      VACATIONS          POPULATIONS          INVITATIONS

4. Genesis says that the moon was made by God on
    day four of _____ .

      CREATION          EDUCATION          ADDITION

5. I can see my _____ when I look in the puddle.

      NATION          REFLECTION          ADDITION

TION / SION

Name

INSTRUCTIONS:
Write the sentence in your best handwriting.

*Genesis says that the moon was made by God on the fourth day of creation.*

Name

INSTRUCTIONS:
Color the circles orange that have pictures that have the
sound of OO.

# REVIEW

Name

INSTRUCTIONS:
Write the OO words below in the correct list. Do they sound like *moon* or *book*?

SPOON, WOOD, FOOT, HOOK, COOK, BROOM, HOOP, MOOSE

*moon*

*book*

**REVIEW**

INSTRUCTIONS:
Match the blend on the left to the correct picture
on the right. There are more blends than pictures.

bl

fl

cl

tr

br

gr

dr

fr

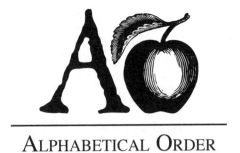

ALPHABETICAL ORDER

Name

INSTRUCTIONS:
Place the following words in alphabetical order.

# A B C D E F G H I J K L M N O P Q R S T U V W X Y Z

action   station   education
vacation   population

1. _____

2. _____

3. _____

4. _____

5. _____

addition   affection   promotion
foundation   mention

1. _____

2. _____

3. _____

4. _____

5. _____

TION / SION

Name _____

INSTRUCTIONS:
Write the sentence in your best handwriting.

*We have an invitation to visit the capital of our nation on vacation.*

# SPELLING LIST 10

Name

INSTRUCTIONS:
Copy the **TION/SION** words below.

creation

section

nation

action

lotion

decision

explosion

vision

division

invasion

Name    *Writing*

INSTRUCTIONS:
Write the words below in the correct columns.
SCOUR, SOUR, COUNT, FOUR, COURT, SOURCE, MOUSE,
ROUND, POUR, TOUR.

*your*                    *house*

TION / SION

INSTRUCTIONS:
Write the sentence in your best handwriting.

The mouse ran in the house to pounce on the snout of the hound.

# REVIEW

_____
Name

INSTRUCTIONS:
Write a word on each line to finish the sentence.
Choose from the following list:
BED, TOP, ROPE, CAKE, PIG, CUP, BAT, FLUTE

A word with a short a is _____ .

A word with a short e is _____ .

A word with a short i is _____ .

A word with a short o is _____ .

A word with a short u is _____ .

A word with a long a is _____ .

A word with a long o is _____ .

A word with a long u is _____ .

REVIEW

INSTRUCTIONS:
The animal friends have gone sailing! Color in
the picture following the instructions below.

Color the cat orange.
Color the pig pink.
Color the horse brown.
Color the frog green.
Color the butterfly purple.

TION / SION

INSTRUCTIONS:
Underline all the TION and SION syllables at the end of the words. Clap out the beats for the syllables and write in the numbers over the vowels. Then read each word.

starvation          invention

reflection          determination

generation          occupation

imagination          qualification

innovation          education

transportation          separation

TION / SION

INSTRUCTIONS:
Underline all the TION and SION syllables at the end of the words. Clap out the beats for the syllables and write in the numbers over the vowels. Then read each word.

correction          interruption

ignition            protection

duration            foundation

translation         information

television          connection

expression          celebration

## MOON MISSION

INSTRUCTIONS:

Fill in the blanks in this newspaper article that could have been written about one special mission to the moon. Use the words in the word bank.

# The Eagle Has Landed

It is a great day in space history. A man took a walk on the moon! President _____ would be so proud of our land since he gave the challenge to America to put a man on the moon. That same year _____ was the first American in space. Now our spacemen have taken one step further. _____ is the first man to walk on the moon. When he got out of the Lunar Module, he said, "That is one small _____ for man, one giant _____ for mankind." Another astronaut named _____ also took a walk on the moon. But, _____ had to stay in the Command Module to drive it. The Lunar Module was the _____. While they were on the moon, they took some _____ to take back. They also put up an _____ on the moon's surface. This successful moon mission was _____.

WORD BANK:

Edwin Aldrin    Eagle    leap    American flag    John Kennedy
Michael Collins    Alan Shepard    Apollo 11    step
Neil Armstrong    moon rocks

399

Name

TEST

INSTRUCTIONS
Circle the correct answer.

1. My family is going on a summer _____ .

   HESITATION      VACATION      EXPLOSION

2. Genesis says that the moon was made by God on day four of _____ .

   CREATION      EDUCATION      ADDITION

3. The man was trimming his _____ .

   BUDGE      LODGE      HEDGE

4. Travis and Brandon made yummy _____ .

   FUDGE      BRIDGE      RIDGE

5. The bird is in its _____ .

   CAGE      SAGE      WAGE

6. Please turn to the next _____ in your book.

   RAGE      CAGE      PAGE

7. When I paid my bill the man gave me _____ .

   HINGE      CHANGE      PLUNGE

8. There is a _____ in the rope.

   CLIMB      KNOT      KNACK

9. I can _____ my own name.

   LAMB      PLUMBING      WRITE

10. Jim uses a _____ to spread his butter.

   KNOW      KNIFE      KNACK

# MOON MISSION

INSTRUCTIONS:

Blast off to the moon with your own rocket! Copy and cut out the templates below on thick, colored paper. Use markers to decorate a paper towel roll and the cut out templates before any gluing is done. Overlap A and B on the cone piece and glue the edge. Attach side pieces and cone piece to a paper towel roll. Students may make tissue paper flames for under the rocket.

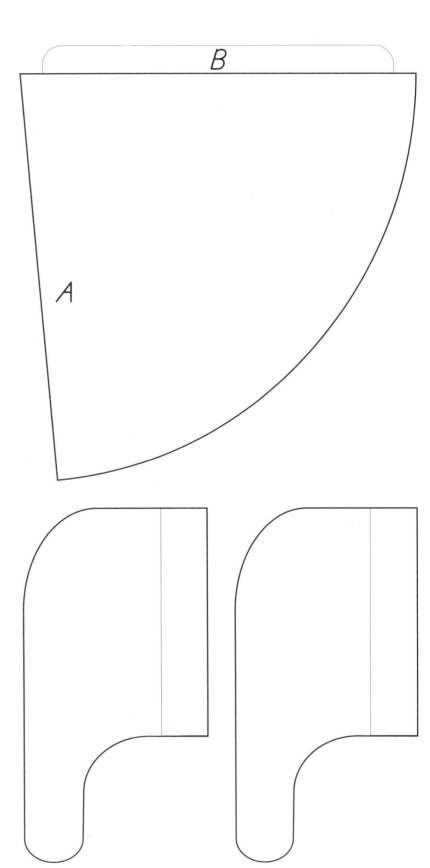

## MOON MISSION

Name _____

INSTRUCTIONS:

Cut out the event strips and the timeline strip. Glue the timeline strip to another sheet of 8.5" x 11" paper. Arrange the event strips in the order in which they occured. Glue the event strips to where they belong on the timeline.

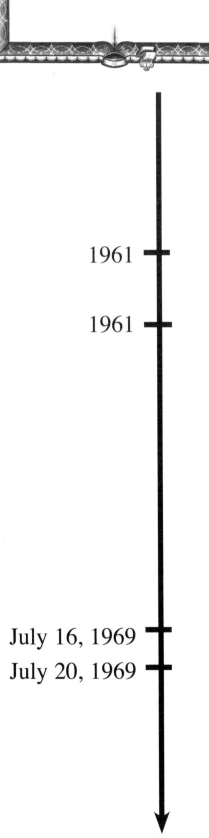

1961

1961

July 16, 1969
July 20, 1969

> The Eagle lands on the moon.

> Three astronauts die
> in an explosion

> President John Kennedy challenges
> America to put a man on the moon.

> Apollo 11 lifts off the earth.

> Alan Shepard was the first
> American in space.

# SPELLING TEST 10

1.

2.

3.

4.

5.

6.

7.

8.

9.

10.

# Ph

Worksheet 141A

Seeing

______________________ Name

INSTRUCTIONS:
PH has the sound of F. Circle the PH in the words below.

| | |
|---|---|
| phone | phrase |
| pharaoh | orphan |
| telephone | telegraph |
| prophet | pamphlet |
| elephant | nephew |

# Ph

INSTRUCTIONS:
Circle the boxes purple that have pictures that have the sound of F made by the PH letter combination.

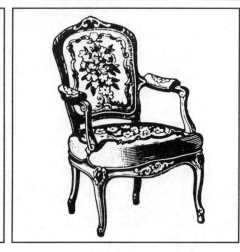

# Ph

| prophet | photo | Special Exhibit: |
| | | shepherd |
| pharoah | phrase | |
| emphatic | emphasis | |
| physical | elephant | |
| philosopher | orphan | |

# Ph

INSTRUCTIONS:
Match the words on the left to the correct picture on the right. There are more words than pictures.

elephant

glacier

pharaoh

telephone

phonograph

social

photo

physician

trophy

ancient

410

INSTRUCTIONS:
Circle the ED in the words below.

tasted          acted

seated          sounded

started         folded

wanted          added

painted         wasted

listed          blasted

If ED is added to a word that ends in D or T the ED sound is heard. If the word ends in silent E preceeded by a D or T the sound of ED is heard. Otherwise ED at the end of a word says D.

411

# ed

INSTRUCTIONS:
Read up and down the word columns.

## ED sound

*Words that end in D or T or a
silent E preceeded by a D or T.*

seat
seated
end
ended
trade
traded
sound
sounded
start
started

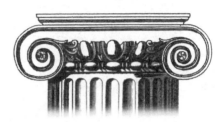

## D sound

name
named
play
played
turn
turned
save
saved
join
joined

INSTRUCTIONS:
Match the words on the left to their correct ED form on the right.

| | |
|---|---|
| call | rained |
| form | formed |
| play | sounded |
| rain | noted |
| rest | acted |
| note | called |
| act | rested |
| sound | played |

413

# ed

INSTRUCTIONS:
Read up and down the word columns.

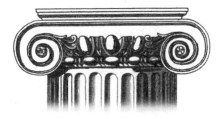

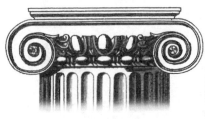

| reach | jump | bake |
| --- | --- | --- |
| reached | jumped | baked |
| | | |
| wish | camp | look |
| wished | camped | looked |

414

INSTRUCTIONS:
Read up and down the word columns.

beard
bearded

carpet
carpeted

button
buttoned

rag
ragged

butter
buttered

fence
fenced

curse
cursed

braid
braided

paint
painted

# ed

Name

INSTRUCTIONS:
Write the sentence in your best handwriting.

*The pharaoh photographed the elephant.*

PH / ED

_____
Name

INSTRUCTIONS:
Circle the word that completes each sentence.

1. Egypt was ruled by a boy _____
   named Tutankamen.

   PHARAOH          TELEPHONE          PHRASE

2. My father _____ corn, peas, and potatoes
   in our garden.

   SOUNDED          PLANTED          TRUSTED

3. Jon talked to his buddy on the _____ .

   PHAROAH          TELEPHONE          ELEPHANT

4. Sue, Jim and Parker _____ on the playground.

   PLAYED          SEATED          NAMED

5. The boys _____ baseball cards.

   BAKED          CAMPED          TRADED

6. The _____ at the zoo ate a ton of hay.

   ELEPHANTS          TELEGRAPH          PAMPHLET

7. My mother _____ a cake for supper.

   BAKED          HATCHED          ROPED

8. Kathy _____ Emily for the nice gift.

   LOOKED          SHOUTED          THANKED

SPELLING LIST 11

INSTRUCTIONS:
Copy the PH/ED words below.

1. photo

2. prophet

3. telephone

4. phrase

5. elephant

6. wanted

7. saved

8. started

9. ended

10. traded

1.

2.

3.

4.

5.

6.

7.

8.

9.

10.

# ph

INSTRUCTIONS:
Read up and down the word columns.

| | | |
|---|---|---|
| some | iron | bearded |
| love | Pharoah | stature |
| give | ragged | Hebrew |
| have | shepherd | cursed |
| one | cawed | decipher |
| won | people | precious |
| plague | physical | |
| guess | hour | |

# ph

INSTRUCTIONS:
Read up and down the word columns.

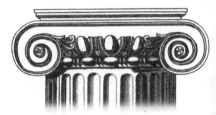

| | | |
|---|---|---|
| quothe | philosopher | appointed |
| dreary | chime | phase |
| ponder | emphasis | dread |
| weary | phony | perished |
| emphatic | finest | nevermore |
| reasonable | orphan | |
| dramatic | foe | |
| mere | wrath | |

QUOTHE THE
PROPHET

INSTRUCTIONS:
In the story most of the sentences rhyme. Read the sentence from the story and write in the blank the word that completes the sentence. Remember, it must rhyme. You may use the story itself to help you.

. But that prophet cawed like a

_____, "Thus says the

Lord, 'Let My people go.'"

. They do physical work all across

my land. There was no burning

bush out in the _____.

. You see, the Lord I do not

know. Do you have a clear

_____?

. I had to make him go away,

to make him see the slaves must

_____.

. You had better flee, you better

run or I'll make an orphan of your

_____.

. He knew no fear at least of me;

God told him his people would be

_____.

7. At least that is what he

claims, but I think he is lacking

_____.

8. He wore me down and drove

me bats; he made it rain frogs and

_____.

9. For before I could even draw my

breath the God of Moses plagued

with _____.

10. He sets them free, slaves nevermore, if they had lamb's blood

upon their _____.

11. And He will bear an iron

rod, for He is Lord, the Son of

_____.

421

QUOTHE THE
PROPHET

Name

INSTRUCTIONS:
Pharaoh and the plagues mobile. Color each picture in,
cut out then tie each circle from a coat hanger using
fishing line.

QUOTHE THE
PROPHET

INSTRUCTIONS:
Write the sentence in your best handwriting.

*Thus says the Lord, let my people go.*

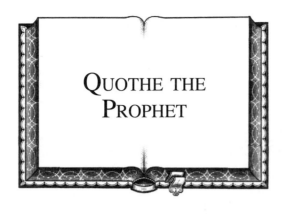

QUOTHE THE
PROPHET

INSTRUCTIONS:
Circle the best answer.

1. Who asked that his people
   be let go?

   PHARAOH

   MOSES

   ABRAHAM

2. Why did Pharaoh want to keep
   the Hebrews?

   THEY DID HIS WORK.

   THEY WERE HIS BUDDIES.

   HE LOVED GOD.

3. Pharaoh said he was strong
   like what?

   A LION

   A BEAR

   AN ELEPHANT

4. Which word was used in the story
   to describe Moses?

   ATHLETIC

   FAT

   BEARDED

5. Which of the following was
   NOT a plague sent by God?

   DARKNESS

   WORMS

   FLIES

6. What happened to
   Pharaoh's son?

   HE BECAME A HEBREW.

   HE BECAME THE NEW PHARAOH.

   HE DIED.

7. How were the Hebrews saved
   from the plague of death?

   THEY PUT LAMB'S BLOOD ON
       THEIR DOORS.

   THEY HID IN CHURCH.

   THEY SACRIFICED AN OX.

8. Whom did God send to release
   His people?

   JUDAS

   HIS SON

   MARY

ed

INSTRUCTIONS:
Read up and down the word columns.

| | | |
|---|---|---|
| wielded | clan | dazed |
| kilt | pirate | finally |
| tromped | protector | overtook |
| toil | terrified | wee |
| daughter | hulk | aye |
| thatched | cleave | plundered |
| Duke | hilt | drab |
| lust | chink | |
| especially | collapsed | |

## THE SWORD OF ROB ROY

Name

INSTRUCTIONS:
In the following sentences, one word is not correct. Cross off the wrong word and above it write the word that makes the sentence true.

1. A boy was staring at a spear behind the glass box.

2. Rob Roy lived in Ireland.

3. Rob Roy was a carpenter.

4. The King wanted to take Rob Roy's land.

5. Rob Roy was thrown in the jail, so another man could take his land.

6. Rob Roy escaped from the Duke and ran off to hide in a cave.

7. Many priests came to join Rob Roy.

8. Rob Roy jumped out at the men from behind rocks.

9. With a club, a huge man came at Rob Roy.

10. Rob Roy stabbed the Duke with his sword.

11. Everyone praised Rob Roy for his victory.

THE SWORD OF ROB ROY

# THE SWORD OF ROB ROY

INSTRUCTIONS:
Complete the crossword puzzle.

ACROSS

. Where Rob Roy was held captive

. A weapon that Rob Roy's men had

. Rob Roy made a plan to _____ from a jail.

. The color of his wife's hair

0. The Duke even took Rob Roy's _____.

DOWN

. What brave men in Scotland wore

. Rob Roy's job

. Where the Duke's men attacked Rob Roy and his men

. Who helped Rob Roy and his men win?

. What the Duke took from Rob Roy

1. The Duke also took Rob Roy's _____.

2. The big warrior came at Rob Roy with an _____.

Name

# REVIEW

INSTRUCTIONS
Write the beginning sound for each picture.

Name

# REVIEW

INSTRUCTIONS
Say the name or label for each picture. Fill in the correct short vowel to finish each word.

l g

tter

n t

l ps

r m

436

SPELLING TEST 11

1.

2.

3.

4.

5.

6.

7.

8.

9.

10.

Name

# REVIEW

INSTRUCTIONS:
Fill in the missing letter group.
SH, CH, TH, WH, TCH

\_\_ess      wi\_\_\_      \_\_ale

 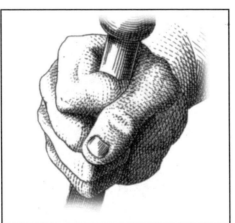 

\_\_ell      \_\_umb      \_\_oe

439

Name

# REVIEW

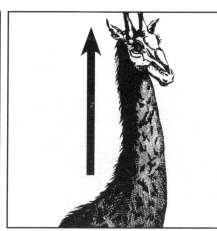

h_____er

r_____

l_____

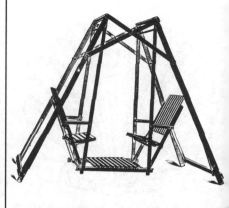

s_____

k_____

sw_____

Name

# REVIEW

INSTRUCTIONS:
Fill in the missing letter group.
CR, FL, TR, SL, FR, DR

\_\_og        \_\_ab        \_\_ed

\_\_ag       \_\_ain      \_\_um

441

Name

# REVIEW

INSTRUCTIONS:
Fill in the missing letter groups.
SK, MP, NK, ST, NK, RK

## wi__

## che__

## sta__

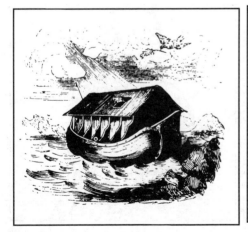

## a__

## si__

## ma__

CAUGHT IN
SMILES

INSTRUCTIONS:
Fill in the blanks in the answers below.

. What is the title of this story?

The title of the story is _____.

. Who is the author of this story?

The author is _____

. Where does this story take place?

This story takes place in _____.

. Name three characters in this story.

Three characters are_____.

. Who was a wicked character?

A wicked character was _____.

. Describe one character other than the wicked one.

_____ was _____.

. What was a problem that Jeanne had?

Jeanne's problem was that _____.

## CONSONANT BLENDS

Name _____

INSTRUCTIONS:
Read up and down the word columns which feature words from the book about Alfred the King.

 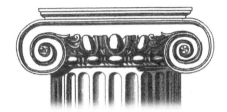 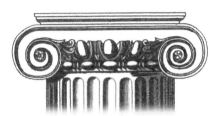

| | | |
|---|---|---|
| Alfred | bliss | black |
| clinging | slick | glen |
| plan | plot | click |
| flag | clang | clack |
| glad | flash | slash |

CAUGHT IN
SMILES

Name

INSTRUCTIONS:
Cut out the pictures and glue them in order in which
they happened on another sheet of paper.

**CAUGHT IN SMILES**

_____ Name

Worksheet 157A

*Comprehension*

INSTRUCTIONS:
Fill in the blanks below.

1. What did Henry rise to be?

   In the end, Henry did rise to be  _____ .

2. How did Jeanne, Henry, and her men escape?

   Jeanne, Henry, and her men played as if they _____ .

3. How did Catherine treat Jeanne?

   Catherine hugged and kissed Jeanne and gave her

   _____ .

4. What did the boys let Henry win?

   The boys let Henry win _____ .

5. How old was Henry when he was brought to Paris?

   Henry was less than _____ .

CAUGHT IN
SMILES

INSTRUCTIONS:
Fill in the answers below.

1. What did the Queen Mother break by throwing it at the wall?

_____

_____

_____

2. Of what land was Catherine queen?

_____

_____

_____

3. Why was Henry taken to Paris?

_____

_____

_____

4. Name two ways in which Catherine tried to spoil Henry.

_____

_____

_____

5. How did Jeanne try to train Henry?

_____

_____

_____

CAUGHT IN
SMILES

INSTRUCTIONS:
People during the time of Henry and Catherine wore different clothes than we do today. Photocopy the figures below on card stock then color a royal outfit. Glue a photo of your face in the space provided and cut out the figure.

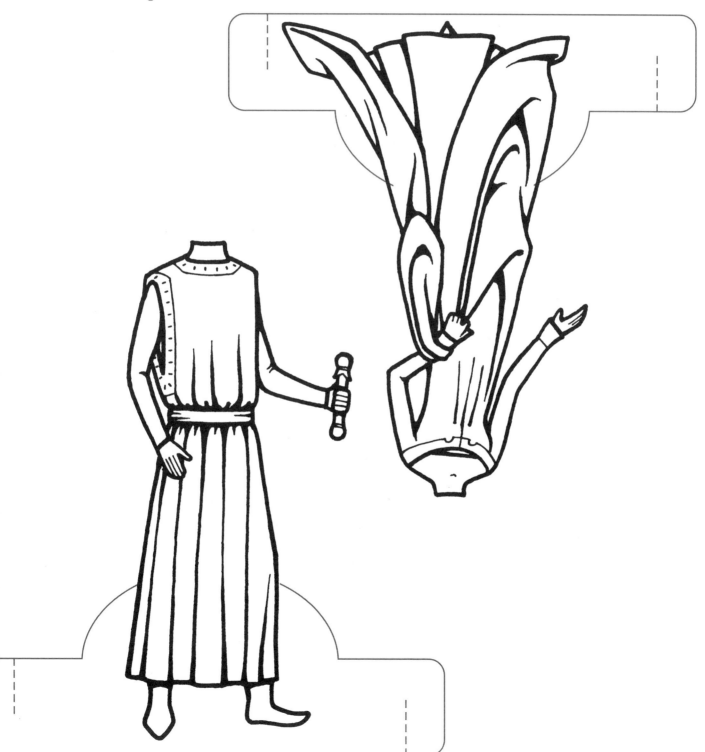

REVIEW

I N S T R U C T I O N S :
Write out the entire alphabet including both upper and lower case letters.

1.

2.

3.

4.

5.

6.

7.

8.

9.

10.

11.

12.

13.

14.

15.

16.

17.

18.

19.

20.

21.

22.

23.

24.

25.

26.

# REVIEW

Name

INSTRUCTIONS:
Color the boxes brown that have pictures that have the sound of OU or OW as in *out*.

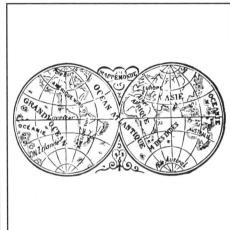

Name

# REVIEW

INSTRUCTIONS:
Fill in the missing long vowel.

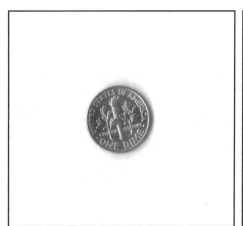

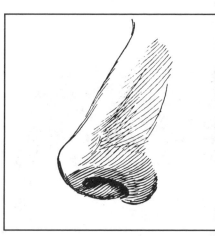

d_me     v_se     n_se

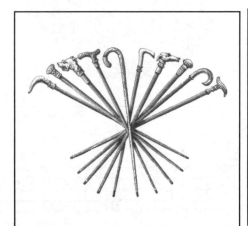

c_nes     gl_be     t_ger

# REVIEW

INSTRUCTIONS:
Match the words to the correct picture.

bear

sheep

sailboat

deer

chair

owl

moose

tree

thimble

wheat

# REVIEW

INSTRUCTIONS:
Color the boxes green that have pictures that have the sound of OO as in *moon* and the boxes red that have the sound of OO as in *cook*.

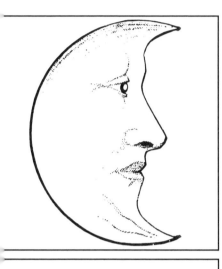

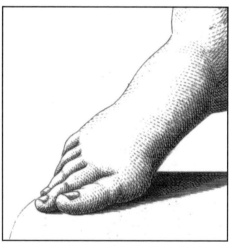

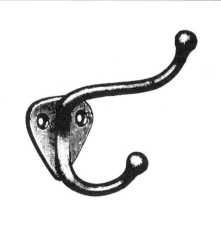

Name

*Hearing*
*Seeing*

# REVIEW

INSTRUCTIONS:
Color the squares yellow that have vowels in them and r
the squares containing consonants.

| A | B | C | D | E | F |
|---|---|---|---|---|---|
| G | H | I | J | K | L |
| M | N | O | P | Q | R |
| S | T | U | V | W | X |
| Y | Z |   |   |   |   |

Name

# REVIEW

INSTRUCTIONS:
Color the silent partner in each word red.

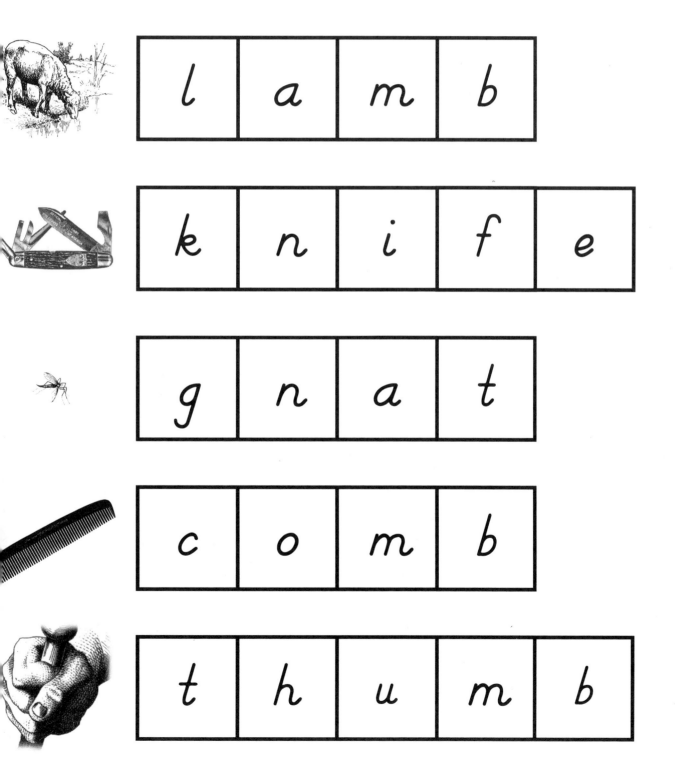

| l | a | m | b |

| k | n | i | f | e |

| g | n | a | t |

| c | o | m | b |

| t | h | u | m | b |

Worksheet 162A

Name     *Comprehension*

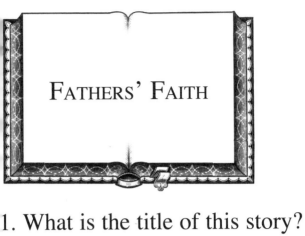

FATHERS' FAITH

INSTRUCTIONS:
Fill in the blanks in the answers below.

1. What is the title of this story?

   The title is _____.

2. Who are the authors of this story?

   The authors _____.

3. Who is the illustrator of this story?

   The illustrator _____.

4. Where are the father and son in this story?

   The father _____.

5. Name the son in the story.

   The son _____.

6. Name two people about whom father told stories.

   Two people _____.

7. What is one problem that Davis has?

   One problem _____

   _____.

8. What is one thing that the boy pretended to do or be?

   Davis pretended _____.

9. Which of the Church Fathers that father told about was your favorite?

   _____.

FATHERS' FAITH

INSTRUCTIONS:
Fill in the blanks in the answers below.

1. How did Davis try to find where he should look on the direction sheet?

    Davis tried to find where to look by _____.

2. Who was Augustine's mother?

    Augustine's _____.

3. What book did Augustine open up to read?

    Augustine _____.

4. What happened when Davis tried to chop down the tree?

    When Davis tried to chop down the tree _____

    _____.

5. To what people did Boniface preach?

    Boniface_____.

6. What was made with the wood from the oak tree that the Germans worshipped?

    The wood from the oak tree _____.

7. What was Chrysostom's nickname?

    Chrysostom's _____.

8. What did the emperor do instead of the festival that he promised?

    The emperor _____.

9. What did Ambrose do when the Emperor came to his church?

    Ambrose _____.

FATHERS' FAITH

INSTRUCTIONS:
Cut out the name plates on the left and run glue along three sides of each strip then place on another piece of paper to create pockets. Then cut out the sentence strips and place each sentence in the correct pocket. You may use the story to help you to remember.

Augustine

Boniface

Chrysostom

Ambrose

He chopped down a tree that pagans worshipped.

He was named Golden Mouth.

His mother's name was Monica.

He preached to the Germans.

His sermons angered the royals.

Led the emperor to repentance.

He used to be a pagan teacher.

He was from Milan.

He opened up the Bible and the part he read made him a Christian.

He left the city to avoid fighting.

He would not let the emperor come in his church.

He had an oak tree made into a church.

461

FATHERS' FAITH

INSTRUCTIONS:
Write a complete sentence to answer these questions.

. What was Davis trying to do while Father was off fishing?

_____

_____

_____

. Whom did Monica pray for each day?

_____

_____

_____

. What was Davis to do while Father was preparing the fish?

_____

_____

_____

. What did the German's worship?

_____

_____

_____

. What did Boniface begin to do that made the Germans angry?

_____

_____

_____

_____

FATHERS' FAITH

INSTRUCTIONS:
Write a complete sentence to answer these questions.

6. Why was Chrysostom called 'The Golden Mouth'?

_____

_____

_____

7. What did Chrysostom do so that the people would not lose their
    lives fighting the emperor?

_____

_____

_____

8. What did the emperor in Ambrose's time say that he was going to do
    to show that he had forgiven the people?

_____

_____

_____

9. What did Ambrose do when the emperor came to his church?

_____

_____

_____

FATHERS' FAITH

Name

INSTRUCTIONS:
Make a diorama of the camping scene from this story.

INSTRUCTIONS:
Match the printed upper case letter to the lower case manuscript letter.

A

B

C

D

E

F

G

H

I

J

K

L

M

N

O

P

Q

R

S

T

U

V

W

X

Y

Z

*e*

*r*

*t*

*y*

*h*

*b*

*u*

*i*

*a*

*o*

*p*

*l*

*k*

*j*

*g*

*f*

*d*

*s*

*q*

*z*

*x*

*c*

*v*

*w*

*n*

*m*

TEST

INSTRUCTIONS
Circle the correct answer.

knot
coat

glut
goose

trophy
trump

ringer
rooster

foam
phone

crown
croon

cow
cud

flog
flower

hope
hook

huff
house

car
chair

not
note

face
faucet

sell
seal

judge
jump

hat
hate

bird
burn

crawl
crab

bait
badge

cage
cape

price
prince

mate
mice

carpet
castle

camp
comb

Name

**TEST**

INSTRUCTIONS
Circle the correct answer.

The elephant searched for
a peanut.

The carriage was stuck
in the mud.

The boy was drumming
on his way to the train.

The judge read what was
written on the paper.

The thin man cleaned
the dirty window.

# Blends

## *sleep*

*Boy Sleeping in the Hay* by Albert Anker (1831–1910)

When Albert Anker was a young boy in the village of Anet, Switzerland, he may have taken a nap or two in the hay of a neighbor's barn. And when he grew up and painted peaceful scenes like this one, he may have wished he was young again – with time to do nothing but lie down in the hay and fall asleep.

When Anker was still a young man, he went to Paris to study art. While there, he developed his own special style of portrait and figure painting and was soon earning a living selling his art. Everyone liked his work because he painted scenes of every day life that people were familiar with.

When Anker was 31 years old, he married Anna Rüefli. They had four children, Louise, Marie, Maurice and Cécile. Anker spent his summers in his hometown of Anet, but he lived in Paris in the winters. He had an art studio there.

He often used his neighbors as models for his paintings. Perhaps the boy in this painting was a boy next door—or maybe even his own son Maurice. Would you like to kick off your shoes and lie down in the hay to take a nap while someone paints a picture of you? Sounds like a nice relaxing job to have, doesn't it?

# +r
## *birds*

Transept Pavement, Heptapegon/Israel

How many birds can you name?

How many birds do you know when you see them?

Have you ever seen an oriole? A bald eagle? A penguin? A chickadee?

Do you know that an ostrich is a bird that can't fly?

Do you know that a rooster is a feathered "alarm clock" that will crow good an loud every morning when the sun comes up?

Do you know that a tiny hummingbird can stand still in the air while it beats i wings, and then zoom away so fast that you can hardly see it fly?

Have you ever heard the song of the wood thrush? The sad cry of the mournin dove? The bright chirping of the robin?

But what kind of birds are these that you see here on the Transept Pavemer mosaic? Their heads look like ducks or geese, but see how long their legs are? The must be water birds of some kind, perhaps herons or storks. These birds are mad out of colored tile. They won't be singing or flying any time soon.

The use of colored tile has a long history in the art of the Middle East, goin back to the Babylonians. After a period of neglect, the art style of mosaics wa revived in the ninth century. Imagine trying to make a picture out of little bits c colored pottery!

# Long Vowels

*pipe*

Still Life with Pipe and Tobacco (detail) by William Michael Harnett (1848–1892)

Get an armful of your favorite toys and dump them on the kitchen table. Arrang them in a way that makes them still look like they were dumped there but that al looks somehow interesting and organized. Then get out your crayons and draw picture of your pile of toys. When you're done, you will have drawn what artists ca "still-life." A still-life is a picture of objects that are just "sitting there." They mig be toys on a table, flowers in a vase, fruit in a bowl, or things like the pipe and tl can of tobacco shown here.

William Michael Harnett was a master painter of realistic still-life. His paintin looked so real that they were almost like a photo would look today—only bette They looked 3-D (three-dimensional). You felt like you could reach out and touch or even pick up—the objects in his painting. Many of his still-lifes used objects tell stories—stories with paint instead of words.

Harnett was born in Ireland in 1838 and came to America (to Philadelphi Pennsylvania) as a baby. When he was a young man he went to New York City study painting at an art school. He painted many still-lifes here in America and the traveled to Europe where his artwork became very popular in Germany.

# ai/ay
## *sail*

---

*Breezing Up* by Winslow Homer (1836–1910)

Have you ever been to the seashore? Have you ever been out on the ocean in boat or a ship? Isn't the ocean big? Doesn't it look like it goes on and on forever How would you like to be out there in those big waves in a little boat with just a sa on it? No motor. No oars to row. Just a sail to catch the wind and move you throug the water wherever you want to go.

Winslow Homer lived most of his life near the ocean. He was born in 1836 i Boston, where the harbor was always filled with ships that were coming and goin He lived in New York City for awhile too—another city by the sea. There he dre many pictures for a magazine called *Harper's Weekly*. He also started painting that time—mostly scenes of farms and country life.

Then he traveled to Paris and then to a seacoast town in England where he wa once again fascinated by the sea. When he came back to America, he moved Prout's Neck on the coast of Maine where he painted and lived for the rest of h life. But he continued to travel to many other places—like Florida and Bermuda ar Nassau—where the ocean waves rose and fell and the tide rolled out and then it can back in. Though Homer painted many realistic scenes of everyday life, most of h paintings were "soaked" with the sea.

# ee/ea

## tree

---

*Apollo and Daphne* by Pollaiuolo (Antonio Pollaiuolo, 1431?–1498; Piero Pollaiuolo, 1443–1496)

The two Italian Pollaiuolo (pronounced *po lee WO lo*) brothers, Antonio and Pier worked together on almost everything they did. And they did a lot. They were stat makers, painters, engravers and goldsmiths. They owned a busy artist's worksh in Florence and always signed their work with one name: Pollaiuolo. Antonio was better artist than Piero, but together they created many beautiful works of art.

Their work illustrated many stories and themes from the Bible and Christian hi tory, as well as from the old stories of the Greek and Roman gods.

*Apollo and Daphne* illustrates an old Greek legend. Apollo was the son of th Greek god Zeus, king of the gods. Apollo fell in love with a mountain nymph name Daphne. But she did not love him—and so she ran away from him. While Apoll was chasing her, she cried out to her father, a river god who lived in the river nearb He heard her, and turned her into a laurel tree so that Apollo could not have her. Th son of Zeus was very sorry, and he promised that from then on all laurel trees woul be forever green. And then he made a wreath of laurel to wear always.

# oo

*book*

---

*Rembrandt's Mother* by Gerard Dou (1613–1675)

Gerard Dou was a very popular artist who liked to paint musicians and other people doing everyday things. He also painted many hermits (people who lived alone in order to spend a lot of time praying to God). He became famous for painting night scenes lit by candelight.

Dou's father painted on glass, and that is where Gerard first became interested in painting. But his real education in painting began when he was about 15 years old. It was then that he started working in the studio of another young artist named Rembrandt. Today Rembrandt is more famous than Dou, but when Dou was alive he was more famous than Rembrandt. And because everybody wanted a painting by Dou, he also became very rich.

His painting of Rembrandt's mother is called a *portrait*. A portrait is a picture that looks just like someone, and it is usually of a person's face. When Dou made this picture of Rembrandt's mother, cameras and photographs had not yet been invented. So the only way to make a color portrait was to sit somebody down and paint a picture of their face. Dou was very good at portraits, but *very slow*. So not many people came to him to have their portraits made. They didn't want to have to sit there all day long!

# oi/oy
## *boy*

---

*Snap the Whip* by Winslow Homer (1836–1910)

Have you ever played Snap the Whip—either running in a yard like these boys or skating on ice or roller skates? It's an old children's game—like Red Rover and Hide and Seek. If you've never played it, ask your mom or dad—or better yet, your grandmom or grandad—to tell you about it.

Winslow Homer, the man who painted this scene of fun and play, was an American artist who is famous for his dramatic paintings of the sea. But he also drew and painted many other things.

When he was a young man, he illustrated pictures for magazines. And when he was 25 he started working for *Harper's Weekly*. They paid him to draw pictures about the Civil War—which was being fought at that time. Homer traveled to war camps and battlefields, drawing what he saw.

After the war he began painting pictures of childhood. He painted children sailing, fishing, farming, going to school in the schoolhouse—and playing Snap the Whip.

Later in life Homer turned his attention more and more to painting pictures of the sea and of life in the towns and villages upon the seashore.

# ou/ow

## crown

*Presentation of Crowns* (detail from the *Trés Riches Heures*) by the Limbourg Brothers (c. 1370–1416)

Three brothers, Pol, Hennequin and Herman Limbourg worked together to create masterpiece of of the fifteenth century. They made the Book of Hours for the Duk Jean de Berry. Berry paid the Limbourgs a lot of money to paint the pictures for thi prayer book—and many other paintings, too. The Duke and his brother the Kin of France gave the most money at that time in Europe to artists to make beautifu things.

The book Pol, Hennequin and Herman made showed what was happening at eac point of the year in the lives of the peasants and the royalty. The brothers used bri liant colors to paint the pictures of everyday life and even used real gold to paint!

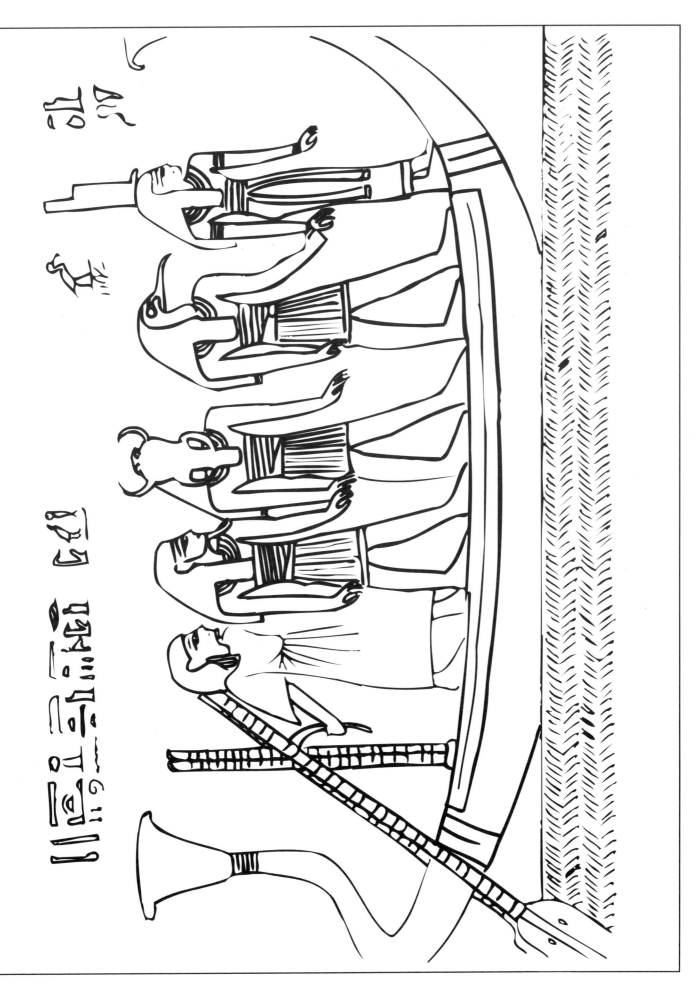

487

# oa/ow

## *boat*

---

*Barge of the Sun on its Night Course*/Tomb of Anhurkhawi

When people don't know God, they make up all kinds of things about the universe he created. They imagine gods everywhere: gods of the stars and the sun and the moon and the trees and the rivers and the winds and the seasons. The ancient Egyptians were like that too. They invented their own gods. Their favorite was the god of the sun, whom they called Ra. They probably like him the best because the sun was up there in the sky every day—so big and warm and full of light. High up in the heavens, travelling daily from the eastern horizon to the west, it stared unblinkingly down upon the whole world.

The paintings like this were made on the walls of the places where they buried egyptian kings they called pharoahs. In these paintings the majority of the people are painted sideways but their eyes are painted looking at the viewer. This picture shows the egyptian gods on a boat taking the pharoah to his final judgement.

# Soft C
## *lace*

---

*Louis XIII* (detail) by Frans Pourbus the Younger (1569–1622)

Frans Pourbus the Younger was a painter. His father, Frans Pourbus the Elder, wa also a painter. They lived in Flanders and the Netherlands. Flanders is not a coun try anymore, but you can see where it used to be if you look at a map of Europe. I was in the north of present-day France and Belgium, with its northern border on th North Sea and its western border on the English Channel.

The Pourbus family painted many pictures from the Bible and about Christianity They also painted many portraits. One of the portraits painted by Pourbus (th Younger) was of Louis XIII, the king of France.

Louis was only a child when he became king, and so his mother, Marie de Médicis ruled the country for him until he got older. Marie loved art, and she introduced he nation to the art of two of her neighboring countries: Italy and Flanders.

Louis is not a little boy in his portrait by Pourbus—but he still looks very youn to be a king. And look at how fancy his clothing is! How would you like to wear big lace collar like his?

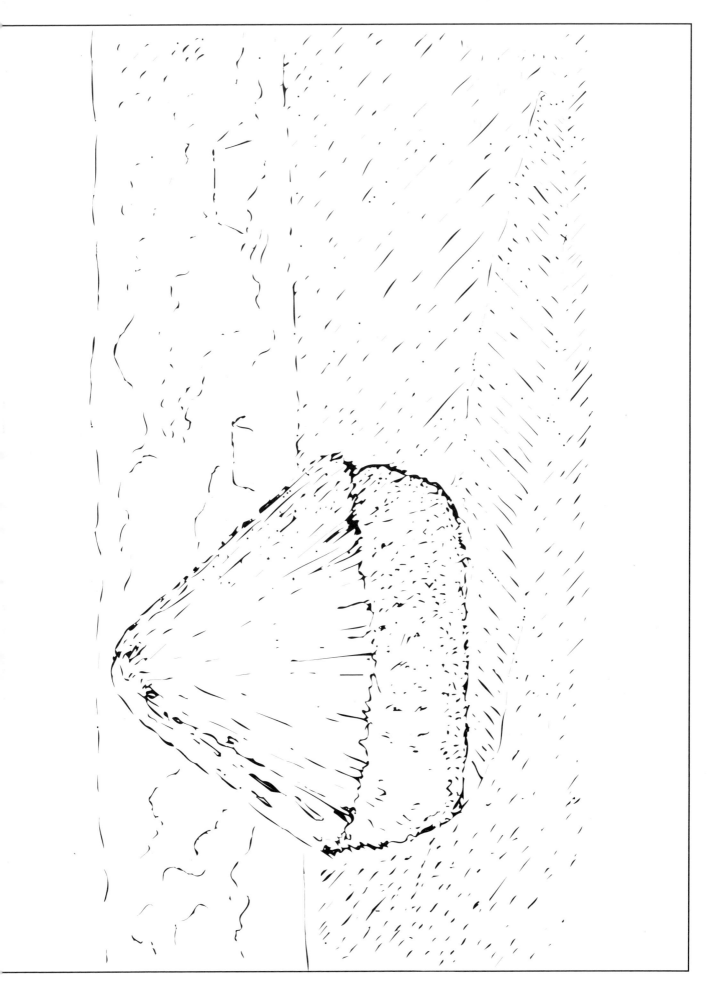

# aw/au/al

## *straw*

*Haystack in Snow* by Claude Monet (1840–1925)

How many ways can you paint one haystack? Claude Monet (pronounced *mo NAY*)painted this one over and over and over again. He wanted to show how one object can look different at different times of the day and in different seasons of the year. So he painted the haystack in the winter, in the summer, in the morning, in the afternoon, at sunset—and many more times.

Monet was an *impressionist*. His art was filled with swirling brushstrokes of color that almost make you blink. The images are sometimes blurry, as if you're looking at them through sleepy eyes or a fogged window. He wanted to paint an *impression* of what things looked like, rather than a realistic picture. He wanted his paintings to make people *feel* instead of think. His artwork created moods instead of told stories.

In 1883, Monet moved to a country home in Giverny, France. There he painted garden scenes. And there he had a waterlilly pond with a footbridge over it.

How many times do you think he painted waterlillies? Well, Monet painted them *so many times* that he once had an artshow with 48 paintings of nothing but waterlillies! And he kept on painting them until he died.

# gh
## *night*

*Starry Night* by Vincent van Gogh (1853–1890)

You have probably seen this painting before. It is the most popular picture of on
of the most famous painters of modern art, Vincent van Gogh.

But when Vincent was alive and pouring out his heart and soul on canvas, hardl
anybody knew who he was. He was often poor, but in a letter to his brother Theo h
once wrote, "I am often as rich…not in money, but rich because I have found in m
work something to which I can devote myself with heart and soul, and which give
inspiration and zest to life."

Vincent's paintings were very impressionistic, full of strong, energetic colors an
shapes. Before committing himself to a life as a painter, van Gogh, the son of a min
ister, had been a preacher in the poor coal-mining districts of Belgium. His brothe
supported Vincent in his painting and they wrote letters to each other. In many o
van Gogh's letters he writes lovely descriptions of his choice of paint colors and th
feelings he attached to each color. Do different colors mean things to you? Wha
kind of night do the colors make your *Starry Night* picture feel like?

# ge/dge
## *bridge*

---

*The Bridge* (detail) by Vincent van Gogh (1853–1890)

When Vincent van Gogh was 27 years old (only ten years before his death), he decided to dedicate himself to a life of painting. But he never really made much money with his art. In fact, he only sold one painting in the ten years of his career. "I cannot help it that my pictures do not sell," he wrote in a letter to his brother Theo.

Today he is famous and his paintings are known all around the world. If Vincent van Gogh were here now, he'd be one of the richest painters alive.

But he didn't want money as much as he wanted to paint. He *loved* to paint. To his sister Wil he wrote, "a painter is someone who paints, in the same way that a florist is in reality a person who loves plants and grows them himself."

His first paintings were still-lifes and pictures of country life. They were painted with dark colors and seem sad. But later, just a few years before his death, he moved to the city of Paris and experimented with impressionism. He painted scenes of the city and the suburbs, and his colors became brighter and stronger. His artwork became more alive and expressive. His most famous paintings come from this later time.

# tion/sion

## adoration

---

*Adoration of the Glorified Christ* (detail from the *Trés Riches Heures*) by the Limbourg Brothers (c. 1370–1416)

Today we can go to the store and buy big calendars with pictures of almost any thing. There are cat calendars and horse calendars and racecar calendars. There ar Dr. Seuss calendars and Winnie the Pooh calendars and American Girl calendar: There are calendars with beautiful photos of mountains and rivers and forests. Yo can find calendars with pictures by famous artists. Calendars of TV stars and popula musicians and singers. Calendars of your favorite cartoon characters and superhe roes. Anything popular *at all* has been made into a calendar.

But did you know that the picture you see here was part of one of the world's firs Christian calendars? This painting of Jesus on his throne in heaven is just one c many beautiful illustrations created by the Limbourg brothers for a devotional praye book called *Trés Riches Heures*. It had prayers and thoughts (and lots of picture: for different times of the day, each day of the week, and for each month and seaso of the year.

But *Trés Riches Heure*s wasn't available in any store. *There was only one copy!*

# ph

## *pharaoh*

*Osiris and Atum Seated with Offerings* (detail)

The ancient Egyptians believed in a god called Osiris. He ruled the world whe[re] people went after they died. The pharoahs (kings) of Egypt believed that they we[re] gods too, and that they were sons of the sun god Ra. But even having a great g[od] like Ra as their father was not enough to get them into paradise. So the Egyptia[ns] put pictures on the tombs of the dead to help them on their way.

Then a custom arose called The Book of the Dead, which was a papyrus boo[k] (often with pictures) that hadwritings to help insure the soul's entrance into paradis[e]. The Book of the Dead was placed in the coffin with the mummified body of th[e] dead.

In the Book of the Dead there is a story about Osiris. It tells how he sits on h[is] throne in a room with forty-two judges. There he judges the heart of each dead pe[r] son to see if he has been righteous and true. If he has not, a monster (half crocodi[le] and half hippopotamus) will devour his soul. Another god named Thoth writes dow[n] the results on a scroll. We know from the Bible that this is not true.